D1244336

DELAYED SENSORY FEEDBACK AND BEHAVIOR

KARL U. SMITH

University of Wisconsin

WILLIAM M. SMITH, Research Collaborator

MARGARET F. SMITH, Editorial Collaborator

W. B. SAUNDERS COMPANY
Philadelphia & London
1962

The following illustrations in this book have appeared in prior publications of the authors and are reprinted or adapted by permission from:

The Behavior of Man, Henry Holt & Co., Inc., 1958.   Figure 3-1.
American Journal of Physical Medicine.   Figures 1-2, 1-3, 1-5, 1-6, 1-7, and 1-8.
Journal of Applied Psychology.   Figures 2-7, 2-8, 2-9, and 2-10.
Perceptual and Motor Skills.   Figure 1-8.
Science.   Figures 2-1, 2-2, 2-4, 2-6, and 5-16.

PREFACE

This book deals with a relatively new experimental approach to a temporal analysis of the properties of behavior and the organization of motion in man. Until recently, research on temporal factors involved in the regulation of behavior has been confined largely to measurements of reaction time and the temporal relationships between external stimuli and overt responses in learning situations. Experimentally established reaction times for specific responses, optimal conditioning intervals and optimal intervals of reinforcement in learning have been accepted in psychology and physiology as having widespread significance in understanding the temporal regulation of motion, and have been used to support theoretical descriptions of behavior in terms of response units organized sequentially by processes of association, conditioning, or reinforcement learning.

Since the years of World War II, when the deleterious effects of time lags between motion and its perceived effects were first observed in tracking systems, a new type of temporal analysis of behavior has developed—that of studying the effects of delayed sensory feedback. The first controlled experiments of this sort dealt with delayed auditory feedback, and more recently the method has been extended to studies of delayed vision, in our own laboratories and elsewhere. The accumulating results of these studies, revealing striking disorganizing effects of delayed feedback, do not fit neatly into traditional interpretations of psychological events. In particular, they cast doubt on some of the basic concepts of learning theory—that human behavior is sequentially organized according to the effects of reinforcement—and seem to demand a reappraisal of all aspects of behavior organization and the learning process. For this reason, we have considered it important to describe the significant phenomena of delayed sensory feedback, as studied indirectly in relation to automated tracking performance, and directly in specific experiments dealing with feedback delay.

Our own work on delayed sensory feedback in behavior has been carried out in a broader context of research on the space organization of motion and its regulation by sensory feedback mechanisms. We interpret our results on temporal displacement of feedback signals as they relate to much more extensive experimental findings on spatially displaced visual feedback. A general presentation of our theoretical description of perceptual-motor behavior, its neural regulation, and the role of sensory feedback in the patterning of motion appears in the book,

Perception and Motion: An Analysis of Space-Structured Behavior, by K. U. Smith and W. M. Smith, published by W. B. Saunders Company. The present book is an extension of one aspect of this earlier work. Thus, we deal with the phenomena of delayed vision and hearing in this larger context of study of the space organization of behavior.

Our program of research on spatial and temporal displacement of vision has been achieved by applying television techniques to behavior research. The general method is to use closed-circuit television systems to supply the performer with a pictorial feedback of his performance. The feedback image can be displaced spatially by manipulating the electronic circuits, the camera lenses, or the television camera itself, and it can be delayed by means of videotape recording systems.

The research described here has been supported by grants from the National Institutes of Mental Health, the National Science Foundation, and the University of Wisconsin Graduate School Research Committee. Preparation of the manuscript has been aided by funds from a Ford Foundation grant.

We wish to acknowledge the cooperation of the University of Wisconsin Television Laboratory for technical aid in maintaining our television equipment, and for permitting the use of their videotape recorder for some of the studies on delayed visual feedback. We also wish to thank the RCA Manufacturing Company Research Laboratories in Princeton, New Jersey, for permitting us to use their equipment and facilities for one of the major studies.

KARL U. SMITH

CONTENTS

CHAPTER 1

THE SIGNIFICANCE OF DELAYED SENSORY FEEDBACK IN BEHAVIOR RESEARCH

Although spatial displacement of stimulus patterns, such as visual inversion or reversal, has been for decades an evident approach to understanding perception and perceptual-motor integration, the use of temporal displacement of movement-produced stimulation is a relatively new idea in behavioral science. By temporal displacement, we mean the introduction of a delay between the execution of a motion and the self-stimulation or feedback produced by that motion. This general idea and experimental approach are so new that their theoretical implications have as yet to be evaluated systematically.

Ordinarily, a motion performed by an animal or individual is a source of several kinds of stimulus feedback, e.g., visual, auditory, cutaneous, or kinesthetic —all of which require finite temporal intervals for the self-stimulation process. A muscular movement sets up a kinesthetic afferent return that denotes the force, position, and magnitude of the movement. Overt motion of the body or its parts also alters the state of external stimulation of skin, eyes, and ears, by means of which the motion may be guided, started, stopped, or controlled in force. When, for any reason, the afferent signals from the movement are delayed beyond their normal transmission time in reaching the receptor or brain, the condition of delayed sensory feedback obtains.

Controlled Studies of Delayed Feedback

Delayed sensory feedback occurs but rarely in natural settings, and only recently has become a subject for laboratory research. Like many other events in science, its experimental analysis has awaited the development of technical devices by means of which it can be controlled and measured. Auditory feedback yielded first to precise experimental control, by means of magnetic tape recording instrumentation. The essential method for delaying auditory feedback is to prevent the subject from hearing the sounds, such as speech, produced by his own movements, to record the sounds on magnetic tape, and to play them back to the subject's ear after a specified delay period. In order that the feedback can be presented to the subject concurrently with his ongoing motion pattern, a dual recording system is used, with the tape passing first through a recording head and then a playback head.

More recently, development of videotape recorders has made possible the systematic analysis of delayed visual feedback. Although this type of research is considerably more difficult and costly than the study of delayed auditory feedback, the procedures are essentially equivalent. The method used is diagrammed in Figure 1-1. The subject sits or stands before the monitor of a closed-circuit television system, watching the image of his own manual movements on

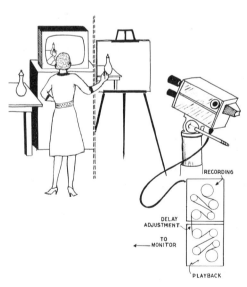

Figure 1-1. Using a dual videotape recording system to delay the visual feedback of motion. The magnitude of delay depends on the length of the interval between recording and playback.

the monitor screen. A curtain is hung between his eyes and hand so that he cannot see his performance directly. A pictorial image of performance is registered by the television camera, recorded by means of a videotape recorder, and then played back to the monitor after a short delay. Thus, the subject tries to perform an organized pattern of motion, in this case drawing a picture, while watching movements that he made before the delay interval. His visual feedback of motion is subject to a constant time lag, which can be varied experimentally from a small fraction of a second to any desired interval. When the feedback from visually controlled movements is delayed in this way, the general effect on performance is disastrous. The motion pattern becomes inaccurate and disorganized, and the individual is likely to show emotional disturbances and loss of motivation.

Problems of Feedback Delay in Human Engineering

The deleterious effects of delayed sensory feedback were recognized first, not in a controlled laboratory situation, but in connection with complicated machine systems developed during World War II. It was early recognized that tracking systems with electromechanically controlled indicators contributed to increased error in tracking performance. Such systems are inadequate from a human engineering standpoint because of the time lag inherent in their controls. Attempts to eliminate this lag either partially or completely, and to assess its importance, have constituted controversial problems in the tracking field, and are significant as well to a theoretical understanding of perceptual-motor integration.

Currently, the problem of delayed sensory feedback in human motion is of great importance in another applied field —that of designing and launching remotely controlled cosmic vehicles. If, for example, a vehicle on the moon's surface is to be controlled from an earth station by means of television eyes, the guidance movements of the operator will be subject to an unavoidable delayed feedback factor due to the time required to transmit electromagnetic signals between earth and moon. This situation constitutes an entirely new problem in human engineering, wherein the human guidance of a machine system is complicated by an absolute feedback delay that cannot be eliminated. The only objective information about the effects of such delay derive from the limited studies of delayed sight and hearing that we shall review in the following chapters.

TRADITIONAL THEORIES OF PERCEPTUAL-MOTOR ORGANIZATION

Studies of delayed sensory feedback represent a new method of analyzing the mechanisms of behavior organization. A basic concern of psychology is to understand how behavior is organized spatially and temporally, how the organized patterns are maintained and controlled, and how they develop in the individual and in the species. When Stratton[71-73] wore his experimental spectacles and mirror systems, he was trying to analyze the essential nature of perceptual-motor integration by spatial displacement of sensory patterns. Similarly, our ultimate concern in studying temporally displaced stimuli is in formulating meaningful concepts of behavior.

Our own theoretical analysis of behavior makes no distinction between perception and motion, but treats them rather as two aspects of the same ongoing process. We believe that perception implies motion—or muscular response—and that motion implies perception. Because most of human behavior involves precisely integrated patterns of perceptual-motor activity, an understanding of the integra-

tive mechanisms is of prime importance to general behavior theory.

Although the phenomena of delayed sensory feedback are relatively new, they promise to be of considerable significance in behavior analysis. We believe that any general theory of behavior should be able to account for the observed effects of feedback delay. However, a cursory examination of conventional theories in psychology indicates that the facts of delayed feedback cannot be incorporated easily into any of them.

Mentalistic Theories

In traditional psychology, interest in the processes of perception has overshadowed analysis of organized motion. The tendency has been to try to describe perception—or perceptions—relative to physical stimuli, and more or less to ignore the problem of motion organization. This one-sided emphasis has been fostered by mentalistic concepts of psychological experience, and the assumption that perception is a function of the central nervous system alone.

Two general theories of motion organization within the mentalistic tradition can be mentioned. First is the belief which was prevalent in early psychological science and is still widely held that motion is produced by conscious volition on the part of the individual. One perceives the world and then one decides to act; control of motion may be based on perception, but is a result of volition. Thus, perceptions and motions are discrete events, related only by the intervention of the conscious self.

A somewhat more refined theory is provided by gestalt psychology, which emphasizes the organizational features of perception. The nature of perceptual organization is determined both by patterns of physical stimuli and the perceiving system. However, here too there is no clear statement of motion organization. Perceptual gestalts occur in the brain, but the mechanisms by means of which they organize motion patterns are not defined.

Although these two general theories—that of voluntary control of motion, and gestalt theory—cannot be translated specifically into physiological or neurological terms, they do contain certain implications about the workings of the response mechanism. Both types of theory put perception in the brain; both assume that perception and motion are discrete and different events; both assume that they are related—integrated—in a temporal sequence. Neither of these points of view would predict any great disturbance of motion due to conditions of delayed sensory feedback. In particular, gestalt theory should predict no disturbance of motion organization with delayed feedback if the delay interval were less than perception time, or the time needed to report the occurrence of perception of stimulus patterns.

Learning and Reinforcement Theory

In recent years, psychological theory has been dominated by concepts drawn from the study of learning. Theoretical constructs derived from investigations of one aspect of behavior organization have been applied almost across the board to many diverse kinds of human activity and performance. Thus, the theories of conditioning,[47] reward reinforcement,[29, 74, 75] stimulus reinforcement,[55] and information reinforcement[21] have been accepted almost without question as general models of behavior integration. The processes of conditioning or reinforcement are assumed to be the primary mechanisms by means of which discrete responses are linked or molded into organized behavior patterns. According to this general view, all human perceptual-motor skills are specifically learned, i.e., built up from the human repertoire of discrete reflexes or responses by means of conditioning or reinforcement effects. The basic organization is sequential; unit

responses are linked in series to form complex patterns.

From the point of view of learning theory, the process of sensory feedback is conceptualized most naturally as a form of reinforcement, or "information feedback" to the individual of the results of his behavior. He moves, and his sensory organs inform him of what he has done. If the movement achieves its goal—if it is accurate—it is reinforced, and consequently more likely to occur another time. If the movement is inaccurate, it is more likely to be eliminated.

The fallacy in this reasoning becomes apparent when we compare the phenomena of delayed sensory feedback with certain other "delay" phenomena studied in relation to learning behavior. A delayed conditioned response is produced by prolonging the interval between the conditioned stimulus (CS) and unconditioned stimulus (UCS). In the normal process of conditioning, as in conditioning a dog to salivate in response to a sound, the optimal interval between the CS (sound) and the UCS (food) is about 0.5 second. If, after the conditioned salivary response to sound is formed, the time interval between CS and UCS is increased, the dog learns to delay its conditioned response to the sound beyond its original latency. A comparable situation in the instrumental learning experiment is known as delayed reinforcement, when the time interval between some adaptive or operant pattern of behavior and the reinforcing reward or punishment is extended. For example, when a rat is trained to press a bar in order to get a food reward, and the interval between response and reinforcement is increased, in the condition of delayed reinforcement, the animal learns more slowly and shows a lower rate of sustained reaction in the situation.

The temporal relationships just described are accepted generally in learning psychology. When the optimal interval between a conditioned and unconditioned stimulus is increased, or when the reinforcement following an instrumental response is delayed, learning still occurs, but somewhat less efficiently. Thus, if we were to equate sensory feedback with reinforcement, we would have to predict that delayed feedback might decrease the efficiency of learning, but that it would not be seriously detrimental to organized behavior.

Actually, the most obvious effect of delayed sensory feedback, even with very short delays of a fraction of a second, is a serious disturbance of behavior. There is nothing in conventional learning theory to account for this disturbance. The temporal relationships and delay phenomena emphasized by learning experiments have involved the modification or control of organized behavior patterns by means of temporal manipulation of extrinsic stimulus factors. Sensory feedback is a critical aspect of the intrinsic behavior organization of the organism, and delayed feedback is seriously disturbing because it interrupts this intrinsic regulation of motion.

Analyses of delayed conditioned response, delayed reinforcement, and other temporal relationships of the learning process have been limited almost entirely to traditional experiments on conditioning or operant learning, usually carried out with animals as subjects, or with human subjects in the artificial laboratory set-ups designed primarily for animals. Such experimental analyses have yielded little of practical or theoretical value regarding the acquisition and control of human performance skills and other organized patterns of human behavior. Our own view is that an understanding of human learning requires first of all some degree of understanding of the neuromotor regulatory mechanisms underlying behavior patterns and skills. Only when we understand something of the nature of response integration can we hope to specify how integrated patterns become reorganized with experience, i.e., how learning occurs.

NEUROGEOMETRIC THEORY

The basic problem of animal motion —or perceptual-motor integration—is to define how it is organized according to the spatial and temporal patterns of the environment. Human motion, in particular, is characterized by its close correspondence to stimulus patterns. This precise geometric organization relative to the environment is a function not only of highly refined sense organs, but requires as well a highly differentiated neuromotor system.

The nature of the neural mechanisms that permit the precise space-structuring of motion has never been established. Accepted ideas of neural integration are based on atomistic concepts of reflexes, chained together sequentially through conditioning, reinforcement, or some equivalent principle. The integrative mechanism is assumed to be the synapse —that blank space between nerve cells that presumably holds the decision-making powers of the behaving system.

It is our firm belief that these conventional views of behavior organization are unsatisfactory on a number of counts. The basic idea that behavior is made up of a series of discrete, unit responses is in itself unrealistic. Behavior at any given time is not a discrete response, but a pattern of responses occurring in many parts of the body. Further, patterned motions are made up not of a number of equivalent responses, but of different types of movement components. No one component occurs independently, but interacts with the other components to define the integrated pattern. The basic organization principle of patterned motion is spatial, not temporal, as is assumed by concepts of sequentially linked reflexes. Finally, the idea that the synapse determines the patterning of behavior is a mysterious—almost fanciful—assumption. There are no objective observations of any activity at the synaptic gaps that would seem to account for the precise, flexible, highly integrated, and extremely rapid patterning of perceptual-motor action that is commonplace in human behavior.

In an attempt to deal with observable facts of motion integration in a meaningful way, we have developed a number of new concepts that are incorporated into what we call neurogeometric theory of motion. The basic assumptions are these: that the spatial organization of motion depends on the mode of action of central nervous system neurons, which respond to differences in stimulation between two specific spatial points; that the temporal organization of motion depends on the various sensory feedback mechanisms of the body, which monitor a motion pattern with respect to the environment and provide for its temporal continuity; and that motion is differentiated into postural, transport, and manipulative components, each of which is regulated by its own neurogeometric system in relation to particular stimulation patterns. By means of its differential detection and sensory feedback functions, the neuromotor system achieves a spatial

and temporal conformity of patterned motion with the geometric, gravitational, and temporal dimensions of space. Any disturbance of this organization motivates the individual to establish new spatial and temporal integrations, and the magnitude of the disturbance defines the degree to which different levels of vital action will be mobilized to adapt the body to the changed conditions.

Neurogeometric Detectors

The first basic concept of neurogeometric theory is that neurons of the central nervous system act as differential detectors sensitive to differences in neural activity at their dendrite endings. Each such neuron is related to two specific points, either within the same or different receptor systems, and is activated when some inequality of stimulation exists between these two points.

This differential mode of action of internuncial neurons is diagrammed in Figure 1-2. The arrows in this figure represent movements of the muscular system

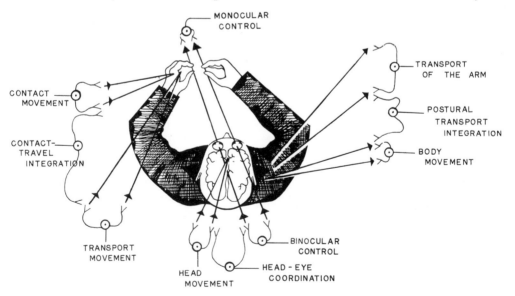

Figure 1-2. The differential mode of action of internuncial neurons. Neurogeometric detectors react to differences in stimulation in the same or different receptor systems, or between efferent and afferent patterns. Thus they detect the negative feedback of movement-displaced patterns of stimulation.

(including various movements of the eyes) that result in stimulation of specific points of the visual, cutaneous, kinesthetic or labyrinthine receptors. The neurons connecting the directional arrows are neurogeometric detectors that react only when some difference in stimulation exists between the two precise points of stimulation with which they are related. Such a neuron does not react when neither point is stimulated, or when both are stimulated equally. Through different types of neurogeometric detector systems, the relative angles of movement of eyes, head, tongue, jaw, arms, hands, fingers, legs, feet, and toes are continuously detected with respect to the effects of gravity, the bilateral symmetry of the body, and the geometric dimensions of hard space.

We assume the existence of at least three types of neurogeometric detectors in the central nervous system. Type I detectors detect differences within a given afferent system, as, for example, between two points on the retina or two points on the skin or within the musculature. Type II detectors detect differences between loci of stimulation in two different types of receptor systems, such as a point of stimulation on the retina and a particular neuromuscular bundle in the shoulder. Type III detectors detect differences between the efferent output of central motor neurons and the sensory feedback of both kinesthetic and exteroceptive stimulation related to the movement triggered by these neurons.

The existence of neurons that specifically detect and control direction of response was originally hypothesized from studies on optical tracking movements of the eyes and head in guinea pigs.[59] Figure 1-3 illustrates the critical experiments that led to this interpretation. A guinea pig with one eye covered was placed in a black and white striped drum. When the drum was rotated toward the uncovered eye, nothing happened (Fig. 1-3a). No tracking (nystagmic pursuit) movements were recorded even though

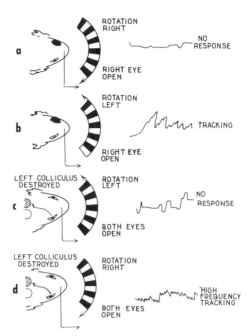

Figure 1-3. Evidence for different types of neurogeometric detectors in the control of visual tracking movements of the head in guinea pigs. *a.* With the left eye covered and rotation of the visual field to the right, no tracking responses are given. *b.* With the left eye covered and rotation to the left, tracking occurs. *c.* With the left colliculus destroyed and rotation to the left, no tracking occurs. *d.* With the left colliculus destroyed and rotation to the right, high frequency tracking responses occur.

the open eye was stimulated. When the drum was rotated toward the covered eye, however, active pursuit movements of the head occurred, as shown in Figure 1-3b.

By surgical procedures, it was demonstrated that this directional system of movement control in the guinea pig is related to the superior colliculi of the midbrain. As shown in Figure 1-3c, with destruction of the left superior colliculus, which receives mainly fibers from the right eye, there were no pursuit movements produced by movement of the environment to the left. The effect was the same as could be achieved by covering the right eye. When the drum was rotated to the right, pursuit movements to the right occurred (Fig. 1-3d), but of quite a different nature from movements made by an unoperated pig with one eye covered. With rotation toward the side of the ineffective eye, the frequency of the nystagmus movements was much higher in the pigs with one colliculus removed than in normal animals with one eye covered.

We now interpret these directional controls of visual tracking in guinea pigs in neurogeometric terms. We assume that each superior colliculus contains Type I (intrareceptor) and Type II (interreceptor) neurogeometric detectors which control pursuit movements toward that side, i.e., in the direction opposite the eye from which it receives its fibers. Thus, even though both eyes are stimulated during rotation of the environment to the right, the right superior colliculus and the left eye control the pursuit movements to the right. It is our opinion that this directional control cannot be entirely visual, but involves also the activity of Type II (interreceptor) detectors which compare loci of visual and kinesthetic stimulation. In addition, Type III (efferent-afferent) detectors are assumed to help regulate the normal timing and patterning of the visual pursuit movements. When the neural record from the left colliculus is abolished by surgical lesions, and the visual field is rotated to the right, marked imbalances in excitation occur in the Type III detectors in the right colliculus. This imbalance produces the increase in frequency of nystagmus movements regulated by the left eye and the right colliculus.

The specific directional control of eye movements by one eye and by one side of the midbrain is not lost in higher animals, but its effects are normally obscured by a more advanced cortical neurogeometric system related to visual pursuit of isolated stimulus patterns. The guinea pig does not pursue single stimulus patterns moving across the visual field. Carnivores and other higher animals do respond to such moving isolated patterns. Removal of the visual cortex in higher animals eliminates focal vision and with it the ability to follow single stimulus patterns, and thus reduces these animals to a visual status not unlike that found normally in the guinea pig.[60, 63]

Figure 1-4 diagrams our concept of the three different types of neurogeometric detectors. In Type I an intrareceptor detector system regulates continuous pursuit or tracking in which uninterrupted movement of a part of the body is achieved by stimulation of adjacent sensory points. The Type I internuncial detectors respond to the differences in stimulation produced by the moving stimulus and thus control the direction and speed of the pursuit movement. Interreceptor detectors (Type II) act in a comparable manner, responding to stimulus differ-

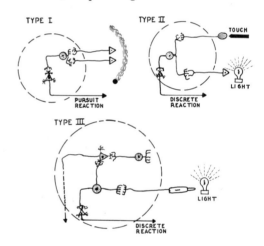

Figure 1-4. Modes of action of different types of neurogeometric detectors in regulating continuous sensory-monitored movements and discrete movements. Pursuit movements are regulated by Type I detectors, which detect differences in adjacent receptor cells, as in the eye or skin. Intrareceptor detectors also detect differences between remote points in the same receptor and thus control discrete responses. Type II detectors detect differences between corresponding space points in two different receptor systems and thus regulate discrete responses. Type III detectors are efferent-afferent detectors which serve to stop and start discrete movements, such as the saccadic movements of the eyes.

ences arising at points in two different receptor systems. We believe that the so-called association centers and association areas of the cortex are made up principally of such interreceptor detectors which regulate patterns of motion in terms of more than one mode of stimulation. The third type of internuncial neurogeometric detector is the efferent-afferent detector. These neurons apparently occur throughout the nervous system. The type diagrammed here bridges the input and output of the nervous system by detecting differences in neural activity between a specific efferent path and a congruent afferent path. Other efferent-afferent detectors are sensitive to differences in activity between an efferent path on one side of the brain and an afferent path on the other.

Several recent studies in neurophysiology have provided evidence for the existence in the central nervous system of neurons that serve the specific function of detecting differences in stimulation. The original discovery was that of Galambos,[23] who described neurons in the auditory centers of the medulla that are very sensitive to time differences in stimulation between the two ears. Lettvin, Maturana, McCulloch, and Pitts[40] have found neurons in the frog's brain that are sensitive only to movement of visual stimuli, and still others that are sensitive to border and contrast effects in visual stimulation. Magni, Melzack, Moruzzi, and Smith[45] have observed direct electroneural effects of the efferent output of the pyramidal system on the dorsal column nuclei (sensory systems of the medulla) in the cat. This relationship suggests to us the action of Type III neurogeometric detectors. Although there is no direct evidence, we believe that the neurons that invade the cochlea and retina from the central nervous system are neurogeometric detectors that sharpen or funnel the input patterns of stimulation by detecting stimulus differences.

Sensory Feedback Control

The significance of sensory feedback in the organization of behavior arises from the fact that most of the stimulus changes to which the individual reacts are produced by his own motion. Every movement produces changes in his physical environment that are detected by the various feedback systems of the body. Feedback signals from the visual, auditory, cutaneous, and kinesthetic receptors provide continuous checks on the spatial and temporal precision of motion patterns in terms of differences that excite the neurogeometric detectors of the central nervous system.

The basic regulatory mechanisms of patterned motion are intrinsically organized and form a part of the genetic endowment of the developing individual. The characteristic motion patterns of different animal species, which are as distinctive as their body forms, are defined by those forms and by the feedback mechanisms that control the organization of motion with respect to the spatial and temporal environment. Motion patterns can be modified to some extent by learning, but the limits of variability are set within a given species. In this respect, the human individual displays far more variability and flexibility in motion than do other animals, but his basic motion patterns are not learned but are a function of his human neurogeometric systems.

From the point of view of neurogeometric theory, sensory feedback is quite a different phenomenon from reinforcement in learning. To equate the two, as has sometimes been attempted by learning theorists, is to overlook the fundamental function of feedback in behavior. Feedback is a critical part of the intrinsic behavior mechanisms of the body; reinforcement is a function of extrinsic stimulus relationships. To define the conditions of reinforcement or learning is not to give a meaningful account of the mechanisms of perceptual-motor integration.

Movement Differentiation and Levels of Neurogeometric Control

A third basic assumption of our theory is that there are organized neurogeometric systems differentiated in relation to postural, transport, and manipulative movements of the body, and that each of these basic movement components is controlled by a particular stimulation pattern. Postural movements are structured primarily by gravitational stimulation; transport movements, by bilateral differences in stimulation on the two sides of the body; and manipulative movements, by the geometric dimensions of hard space. All motions are a product of the integration of these three components.

As shown by the diagram in Figure 1-5,

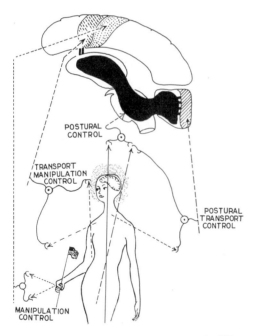

Figure 1-5. The levels of neurogeometric differentiation of the brain for control of posture (relative to gravitational stimulation), body transport (relative to differences in stimulation on the two sides of the body), and manipulative movements (relative to the properties of hard space).

we assume that the three movement components have distinctive levels of differentiation and integration in the brain. Anatomically older parts of the brain (black areas) regulate postural movements with respect to their gravitational control. Newer bilaterally differentiated parts of the cerebellum and cortex regulate transport movements and integrate them with other component movements. The cerebellar differentiation (heavy lines) integrates body transport and postural control, while the forebrain differentiation of the transport system (premotor areas of the cortex) integrates transport movements with manipulative activities of the head, eyes, hands, and feet. The pyramidal system specifically controls fine manipulation. In general, we believe that the different sensory projection systems of the brain are specialized Type I and Type II neurogeometric systems primarily involved in three-dimensional manipulation and orientation of exteroceptors with relation to patterns of stimulation.

STIMULUS DISPLACEMENT AS AN EXPERIMENTAL METHOD

A critical experimental method for analyzing the sensory feedback mechanisms of motion is to displace stimulus patterns, either spatially or temporally, from their normal relationships and record the effects on behavior. Among the functions that can be studied are the individual's tolerance for displacements of various kinds, and his ability to adapt to various degrees of displacement.

Spatially Displaced Visual Feedback

The analysis of spatially displaced vision, i.e., conditions of inversion, reversal, or other displacement of the visual field, is a long-standing problem in the study of behavior, as old as experimental psychology. The problem was first delineated by philosophers and physiologists of the last century, including Johannes Müller, Lotze, Wundt, and Helmholtz, who speculated about the bases of space perception and of perceptual orientation relative to the inversion of the retinal image. Most experiments in this area, such as those of Stratton,[71-73] Ewert,[17] Siipola,[53] Snyder and Pronko,[67] and Kohler,[32-35] were conducted primarily to determine the effects of visual displacement on perceptual orientation, while the overt behavioral effects were of only incidental interest.

During the past decade, we and our co-workers[56, 57, 65, 66] have been interested in developing more precise techniques for analyzing displaced vision, in which the conditions of displacement can be specified and controlled, and the behavioral effects quantified. Closed-circuit television has proved to be admirably suited to these purposes. A televised image of performance can be spatially displaced in almost any conceivable way, either by manipulating lenses, or by moving the camera itself with respect to the performance field. The visual (televised) image thus can be inverted, reversed, or rotated angularly. Also, the locus of vision can be shifted from its normal orientation by moving the camera, much as if the eyes were removed from the head to watch bodily movements from different positions about the room. Along with the television equipment, electronic motion analyzers have been used to provide accurate measures of performance.

THE CONCEPT OF NORMAL DISPLACEMENT IN MOTION ORGANIZATION. Our interpretation of experimental conditions of displaced vision is that they represent nothing more nor less than exaggerations of normal visual conditions. All motion is regulated in terms of motion-generated geometric displacements of stimulus patterns. Further, there is no one "true" orientation of the visual field with respect to the various spheres of bodily ac-

tivity. Patterned motion can be carried out normally under a wide range of visual displacements, due to changes in position of the eyes with respect to the head, head with respect to the body, hands with respect to the body, or head, or eyes, and so on. Thus, there is a variable range of visual displacement that must be considered normal for ordinary performance. With our television methods, we have demonstrated how the limits of such normal visual displacement vary according to the dimension of displacement, and the type and complexity of motion.

Figure 1-6 illustrates how closed-circuit television has been used to determine normal and breakdown ranges of displaced vision. The RCA Vidicon camera, shown in the upper right of the photo-

Figure 1-6. The application of closed-circuit television to the study of motion in displaced visual fields. The camera is mounted on an overhead dolly. The subject, shown here tracing a star pattern, cannot see her own hand directly, but must watch her movements in the television monitor. The televised image can be inverted, reversed, or both inverted and reversed (as shown here) by means of switches mounted on the camera.

graph, is suspended from an overhead dolly with its lens directed toward the subject's hand tracing a star. The durations of motions in different directions are recorded on the clocks shown in the foreground. The subject cannot see her own motions directly, but must watch her performance in the television monitor, shown inside the cloth booth. The monitor image can be inverted, reversed right to left, or inverted and reversed simultaneously by means of switches located on the side of the camera. Further, the locus of vision can be displaced by moving the camera to different points in the room. Using this latter procedure, we can determine the "normal" range of angular displacement of the locus of vision in different planes, and the angles of displacement at which movement breakdown occurs.

The diagram in Figure 1-7 shows how the camera can be moved to different positions in a horizontal plane, with the performance situation at the center of the angular displacement. A position of 0 degrees would have the camera located directly behind the subject, pointed down over his shoulder, and other displacement angles are measured from that position.

30°   90°

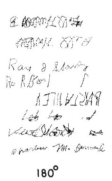

180°

Figure 1-8. The effects on handwriting of displacing the locus of vision 30 degrees, 90 degrees, and 180 degrees in a horizontal plane.

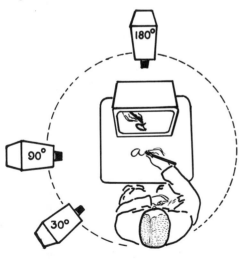

Figure 1-7. Using closed-circuit television to displace the locus of vision.

The camera is elevated above the writing hand, and given a vertical tilt corresponding to the normal line of sight. The subject cannot see his hand directly because of a screen mounted between eyes and hand, but sees his hand in the monitor as if his eyes were located in the different camera positions. In the original television experiment of this sort,[66] handwriting records such as those in Figure 1-8 were obtained. With the camera at a 30-degree angle, the displacement had little effect on the writing. At 90 degrees, the writing of most subjects was completely illegible, while at 180 degrees (at which angle the writing appears inverted), the legibility of the writing was also very poor.

This and other studies have disclosed some significant facts about displaced vision. First, there is a range of displacement within which little, if any, disturbance of perception and movement occurs. Second, there are some positions of angular displacement of the visual image or of the locus of vision to which most subjects show little, if any, adaptation. In these positions, motions requiring visual control break down more or less completely. Third, the breakdown angles of displacement of the locus of vision vary with the type and complexity of motion, and the plane of displacement. For example, the breakdown angle of transport movements in assembly motions is around 60 degrees or a little more, whereas writing begins to deteriorate at angles around 30 degrees. The breakdown angles also vary according to the plane of displacement. When the locus of vision is displaced in a vertical plane by moving the camera in a circle extending up and over the workplace, there is far less effect on all motions than with the horizontal displacements described above.

Studies on motions requiring continuous visual control (e.g., reproductive drawing) show that motions are affected to some extent by small angles of displacement even though no breakdown occurs. When the camera is displaced slightly from its "normal" position directly behind the subject's hand, and the subject is asked to draw a true circle or to reproduce the outline of some object, he will distort his drawing to compensate for the angle of the displacement. That is, he draws the object so that it appears "right" in the television monitor. These compensatory effects occur at displacement angles of 10 to 15 degrees.

We have made many different experimental observations on spatially displaced visual feedback in motion, in which we have shown that the effects of such displacement depend on the type and degree of displacement, the complexity of the movements involved, the direction of movement relative to the conditions of displacement, and the overall orientation of the motion pattern relative to the conditions of displacement. All of our results have provided support for our theoretical description of the space-structured organization of motion and its neurogeometric basis.[56, 57, 62]

Temporally Displaced Sensory Feedback

Neurogeometric theory assumes that the primary organizational factor of patterned movement is spatial, for neurogeometric detectors react in terms of stimulus differences at particular loci. However, the spatial precision of motion is limited by time variables, inasmuch as sensory, neural, and motor processes all require finite intervals. In other words, a movement that is made to equalize a discrepancy between two sources of stimulation is accomplished only after a finite temporal interval. Furthermore, the feedback control of the succeeding movements in a pattern takes additional time. Thus, the precision of motion in conforming with environmental demands is limited not only by spatial factors, but by temporal factors, and as the spatial precision of the motion is increased, its time requirements are correspondingly more precise.

Further assumptions can be made concerning the spatial and temporal relationships in motions of different kinds, depending on the neurogeometric system regulating them. There are basic differences between continuously controlled and discrete motions. Continuously controlled motions are assumed to be dependent on proximally located Type I neurogeometric detectors, whereas discrete movements are regulated by distantly located Type I (intrareceptor), Type II (interreceptor), or Type III (efferent-afferent) detectors. The discrete motion is made in step-wise fashion, and its essential characteristic is that its manipulative components are functionally separated in time from its transport components. In the continuously controlled motion, however, the transport movements overlap in time the positioning or manipulative movements. Because the feedback relationships involved in continuous motions are quite different from those involved in discrete motions, we would expect differential effects of feedback delay.

Many of these assumptions can be tested experimentally by systematically delaying the sensory feedback of motion. Neurogeometric theory predicts that in continuously controlled motion, the normal near-simultaneous or synchronous stimulation of neurogeometric detectors represents the optimal condition of movement integration, so that any interruption or delay in the normal feedback time will have some deleterious effect on the learning and performance of that motion. The effects of the delayed feedback on a given movement will be a direct function of its geometric precision, so that more precise movements will be affected far more than less precise movements. We predict also that the greater the geometric precision and refinement of a movement, the more quickly it will deteriorate with increasing delay intervals. Consequently, many precise movements will be seriously affected by delay times of a magnitude less than reaction time, or perception time. In general, the greater the velocity of a continuous visually controlled movement, the shorter the delay interval that will affect it adversely. The effect of feedback delay on any motion will be greatest when it approximates the movement time of the geometrically most precise component in the motion.

In addition to these quantitative changes, neurogeometric theory also predicts certain qualitative changes in movement organization that are likely to occur under conditions of delayed feedback. First of all, we expect persisting variability in motions when either spatial or temporal disturbances are introduced into the neurogeometric control system. No smooth learning curve could be predicted for subjects trying to adapt to the distorted conditions. Delayed feedback probably will lead to changes in the temporal pattern of interacting component move-

ments. One type of integrative change that we expect with a delay interval of maximal effect is a shift from continuously controlled motion to discrete, jerky movements. This shift would occur because of the greater effect of feedback delay on continuous movements than on discrete movements. The effect of delay on continuous motion is comparable to the effect of interrupting the source of stimulus guidance. Both of these conditions lead to loss of continuous control of movement with the substitution of discrete movements. Finally, one can predict that with feedback delay in visually controlled movements, the control could shift from the visual system to some other afferent channel, while general task orientation is still defined by the delayed visual stimulus. It seems likely that under some conditions of delayed visual feedback, the control of movement might shift back and forth from visual to other sensory modalities to reduce the disturbing effects of the visual delay.

In the next four chapters, we shall review the available objective information on the effects of delayed sensory feedback. We shall discuss first, in some detail, the problem of feedback delay in relation to tracking performance. We shall try to assess the specialized studies on tracking and the design of tracking systems in terms of their significance to general theories of perceptual-motor integration and behavior. Next we shall describe the experiments specifically designed to analyze the effects of delayed sensory feedback, both auditory and visual. We believe that this area of research holds great promise both for psychological theory and for applied problems of human engineering.

SUMMARY

1. Experimental delay of auditory and visual feedback has been accomplished

by means of magnetic tape recording and playback of the auditory or visual signals.

2. Delayed visual feedback has been an applied problem since the development of electromechanically controlled tracking systems in World War II. A current problem is concerned with delayed feedback signals from earth-controlled roving space devices.

3. The phenomena of delayed feedback are of considerable significance for theories of perceptual-motor integration and behavior. Conventional psychological theories cannot account for the disturbance caused by delayed feedback.

4. Learning theory tends to equate sensory feedback with reinforcement, and thus would predict that learning would occur even if the feedback is delayed. The disturbance that results from feedback delay indicates that it interrupts the intrinsic patterning of behavior.

5. The spatial and temporal organization of patterned motion cannot be accounted for by concepts of unit responses linked together sequentially according to synaptic action.

6. Neurogeometric theory proposes that motion is differentiated into postural, transport, and manipulative components, and that its integration depends on the sensory feedback mechanisms of the body. Central nervous system neurons are assumed to respond to differences in stimulation arising at two specific points.

7. Three kinds of neurogeometric detector neurons are postulated: Type I, intrareceptor detectors, associated with two points in the same receptor organ; Type II, interreceptor detectors, associated with two points in two different receptors; and Type III, efferent-afferent detectors, associated with a point of efferent output and a corresponding afferent feedback point.

8. Continuous pursuit movements would depend on Type I detectors; discrete movements would depend on Type II or Type III detectors.

9. Patterned motion depends upon sensory feedback regulation—visual, auditory, cutaneous, and kinesthetic. The developing individual is endowed with basic motion patterns that are defined by heritable neurogeometric feedback mechanisms.

10. Postural, transport, and manipulative components of motion each have their own organized neurogeometric systems, and are controlled, respectively, by gravitational stimulation, bilateral stimulus differences on the two sides of the body, and the geometric dimensions of hard space. Older parts of the brain control postural movements, bilaterally differentiated areas of the cerebellum and cortex control transport movements and integrate them with other components, and the pyramidal and sensory projection systems control manipulation.

11. Spatial and temporal displacements of stimulus patterns are critical methods for analyzing feedback mechanisms.

12. Studies of displaced vision (inversion, reversal, or rotation of the visual field; displacement of the locus of vision) by television methods indicate that there is a normal range of visual displacement within which motion is disturbed little if at all, and a breakdown range in which serious disturbance occurs.

13. The effects of spatial displacement depend on the type and degree of displacement, the complexity and direction of movements, and the overall orientation of the motion pattern.

14. Neurogeometric theory assumes that the spatial precision of motion is limited by temporal variables, due to time required for response and sensory feedback processes. Feedback relationships are quite different for continuous and discrete motions, and thus there are differential effects of feedback delay for different kinds of motions.

15. The assumptions of neurogeometric theory provide the basis for a number of predictions about the quantitative and qualitative effects of feedback delay that can be tested by systematic experiments on delayed feedback.

CHAPTER 2

DELAYED VISUAL FEEDBACK IN TRACKING PERFORMANCE

The phenomena of delayed visual feedback received their first specific recognition during World War II, in relation to some very practical human engineering problems of tracking behavior. Tracking or steering motion can be as simple as following a moving object with the hand or eye, or steering a simple vehicle along a path. The human visual-neuromotor system permits highly precise following movements of this sort, wherein the accuracy is checked and regulated constantly by means of the sensory feedback mechanisms.

Tracking behavior becomes a technological problem when the machine to be pointed or steered is too heavy or too remote for direct or easy manipulation

16

by the human operator. Thus a ship, aircraft, or heavy gun must incorporate some kind of power system to enable the steersman to control its direction and rate of movement. Power steering in automobiles is a common example of this indirect control of a machine system. Unfortunately, these technological improvements in tracking systems have given rise to a very real and very difficult behavioral problem—that of delayed visual feedback. The introduction of a power system between the operator's control movements and the response of the machine also introduces a lag in sensory feedback to the operator as to the effects his movements have produced. Unless some special provision is made, e.g., by means of a dial indicator, to reduce or eliminate this lag, the accuracy and efficiency of the tracking performance are affected adversely.

The problems of power steering are minor, however, compared with those that arise in connection with so-called velocity tracking devices. In systems of this sort, movements of the operator generate a rate of movement or velocity of the machine, so that it continues to move in a certain direction until a correctional control movement is made. That is, in velocity tracking, the operator does not steer his machine directly, but only indirectly by means of controlling the velocity generated by a motor. In systems of this sort, the delay between action of the operator and visual feedback of its effects is of such magnitude that tracking performance is seriously hampered.

In an effort to eliminate the errors of velocity tracking, engineers in World War II developed what is known as "aided" tracking, in which a movement of the operator positions the device directly, without delay, but also generates a rate of movement in the device by means of the motor system. In following a moving target, however, the rate of tracking movement must be adjusted to the speed of the target, and information about the rate generated by the operator is still delayed in aided tracking, even though there is immediate feedback about the initial position assumed by the tracking device.

The relative accuracy of different types of tracking systems has been the subject of many experiments and theoretical analyses during the past two decades, and a considerable body of tracking literature has accumulated. We believe that the critical factors defining tracking performance are the temporal relationships involved in the behavior of the tracker.

Accordingly, we shall attempt to analyze tracking problems in terms of the phenomena of delayed visual feedback.

TYPES OF TRACKING SYSTEMS

Tracking performance is studied in the laboratory by means of set-ups such as that shown in Figure 2-1. In the tracking system illustrated, the operator sits in the chair at the left and manipulates the hand control so as to make a cursor or indicator follow a moving target. The target moves in a predetermined oscillating circular path, defined by the design of a cam fitted on a motor in the target generator mechanism. Thus, the tracker sees the target oscillate back and forth in a circular path and tries to adjust his handwheel control so that the cursor always points toward the target.

In order to measure the accuracy of performance in such a system, the target drive mechanism is equipped with a small selsyn motor, of which the field turns with the target and the rotor moves with the cursor. When the cursor is pointed directly at the target, there is

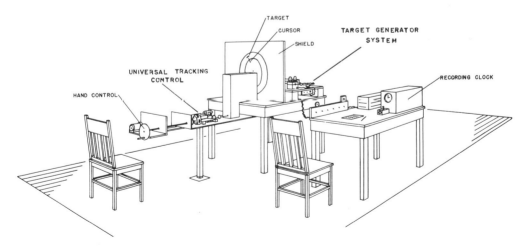

Figure 2-1. An experimental set-up designed to compare different types of tracking with direct, velocity, and aided control. The subject sits in the chair to the left, operating the hand control to make the cursor follow the target, which moves in a random circular course. Tracking error is recorded both graphically and in terms of an integrated error score.

no electrical signal generated by the selsyn, but when the cursor and target are not aligned, an electrical signal is generated of a magnitude proportional to the deviation between cursor and target. This error signal is transmitted to a receiver selsyn and produces oscillations in an arm mounted upon it. A rotating contactor unit moving under this oscillating arm activates a time clock in proportion to the accuracy of alignment of target and cursor, giving an integrated time measure of tracking accuracy.

A graphical record of error can also be obtained in such a tracking system. A second receiver selsyn, activated by the error signal, moves a recording arm that imposes a graphical line on a moving waxed paper tape. This "analogue" record of performance can be analyzed for frequency and magnitude of error.

The "universal tracking control" of this system permits various types of control of the cursor—direct, "velocity," and "aided" control. In direct control, the handwheel is linked directly to the cursor, so that movement of the handwheel produces immediate movement of the cursor in the same direction. The system can be shifted to velocity control by throwing a small gear shift and adjusting a belt drive mechanism. Now the handwheel adjusts the arm of a potentiometer, which in turn controls the direction and speed of movement of the cursor. The sensitivity of such control can be adjusted by means of speed controls on the motor drive mechanism of the cursor. By means of another gear shift and belt drive adjustment, the system can be changed to aided tracking. In this case, movement of the handwheel positions the cursor immediately and directly, in proportion to the magnitude of the control movement, and also activates a motor-drive mechanism that causes the cursor movement to continue. Now, when the tracker moves his handwheel, the cursor moves immediately in response

but then continues to move at a rate depending on the magnitude of the control movement.

Direct Pursuit Tracking

The three drawings in Figure 2-2 compare the basic design components involved in three types of tracking systems —direct pursuit tracking, velocity tracking, and aided tracking. In direct pursuit tracking the operator controls a cursor in following a target in much the same way as the driver of a Model-T Ford steered his car along a narrow 1920 roadway. Every jiggle of the control wheel produces a corresponding movement of the device being steered. Moreover, when the operator moves his handwheel, the cursor moves immediately in the same direction, with no delay.

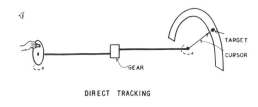

DIRECT TRACKING

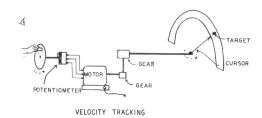

VELOCITY TRACKING

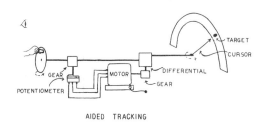

AIDED TRACKING

Figure 2-2. Types of tracking systems: direct pursuit tracking; velocity tracking; aided tracking.

Velocity Tracking

When guns for planes and ships in World War II were developed beyond the point where they could be sighted efficiently by eye or by computational tables, it became desirable to drive the gun mount with a motor and to provide the gunner with a sighting device that would direct the gun through control of this motor. Such a gun-laying system is a velocity tracking system, involving the components illustrated in Figure 2-2. In this case, the operator tracks a target with some sort of cursor or sighting device, but can move the device only by controlling the direction and speed of a motor. Now he cannot position his cursor or gun directly; he can only speed up or slow down the motor, thus changing the rate of movement of the cursor, or he can reverse its direction of movement.

In a velocity tracking system of this sort, the novice operator feels lost, because his control movements seem loosely connected with the gun or cursor. One of the rare experiences in World War II was to climb into the Sperry belly turret of the B-17 and try to aim the turret with its two .50-caliber guns by means of the velocity tracking system with which it was equipped. It was as good as a carnival ride. No matter what the novice gunner did, the turret and guns gave him the wrong answer about his movements. If he thoughtlessly tried to direct the guns at the target in a hurry, he might find himself overshooting in a wild spin. The basic trouble was that the operator was receiving delayed visual feedback of his motions, occasioned by a lag of some 0.5 to 1 second between the execution of control movement of the sight and the effect of this movement on the action of the turret.

In a velocity tracking system, the feedback delays produced by accelerating the motor from a zero velocity to some finite speed, by changing its speed, or by shifting the direction of movement are vari-able and can be of considerable magnitude if the tracker tries to move his cursor or gun over a relatively long distance. Thus, the tracker must try to adapt not just to delayed feedback, but to delays of variable magnitude. For this reason, velocity tracking is an extremely poor system for directing any kind of mechanism, particularly if the tracker must control movements in two dimensions, as he did in the Sperry belly turret of the B-17.

Aided Tracking

In spite of the control problems of velocity tracking, some engineers in World War II were convinced that any type of aided tracking was superior to unaided or direct pursuit tracking. They believed that partial automation of the steering function would simplify the operator's task and thus reduce errors. Accordingly, they tried to improve on velocity control by designing a mechanism known specifically as an aided-tracking mechanism. This type of control is also illustrated in Figure 2-2. In this system, the operator moves his handwheel as he does in direct pursuit tracking to make an immediate positional adjustment of the cursor. However, this same movement also controls the direction and speed of a motor system that is connected to the cursor through an integrating system. Thus, movement of the handwheel both positions the cursor and imparts to it a rate of movement by means of the motor system.

In aided tracking, the experience of the operator is quite different from that with either direct or velocity tracking. In trying to follow the target, he can position the cursor immediately by moving the handwheel, but then the cursor continues to move due to the action of the motor system. This secondary effect is subject to the delayed feedback factor, for the operator cannot see immediately the final effects of his own movement. That is, he cannot at once see a *rate* of movement. Further, the speed of movement generated by the aiding motor system is not the same as the rate of the immediate positioning movement of the cursor. This discrepancy between immediate feedback of the positioning movement and delayed feedback of the aided control of the cursor has given rise to the complicated and controversial literature dealing with the problems and theory of tracking devices.

ANALYSIS OF THE TIME FACTOR IN AIDED TRACKING

One of the original design problems that had to be considered in the initial phases of development of aided-tracking systems was to specify the rate of cursor movement that would be generated by a control movement of standard magnitude. The relation between magnitude of positional change of the cursor and the generated rate of cursor movement is expressed as a time constant, known as the aided-tracking ratio or aided-tracking time constant. For a given tracking system, this ratio equals the unit change in position of the cursor over the displacement per second generated by that unit change. Thus, a time constant of 1 would indicate that a control movement that displaces the cursor by one unit of distance would also generate a velocity of one unit per second. As the generated velocity of cursor movement per unit positional change increases, the aided-tracking ratio decreases. A zero value of the ratio indicates that the system is altogether velocity controlled, i.e., that it is a velocity tracking system. The higher the value of the ratio for a particular system, the slower is the movement generated by a unit positional change.

To illustrate the meaning of the time constant in aided-tracking performance, let us take as an example a system with a ratio of 1. If the operator moves his handwheel control one unit of distance very quickly, the cursor will move one unit of distance in a negligible amount of time. However, the control movement has also generated a rate of one unit per second, so that, if the operator makes no further adjustments, the cursor will have moved approximately two units of distance after the first second, and will continue to move one unit per second thereafter.

Optimal Aided-Tracking Ratio

One of the principal theoretical controversies in the tracking field, which arose with development of the first aided-tracking mechanisms designed for microwave radar systems, has been whether or not there is an optimal aided-tracking ratio for maximal accuracy of the tracker in all kinds of devices and under all conditions. This problem is a very practical one when it comes to designing tracking systems. It is also of theoretical interest to psychologists and human engineers who have been concerned with the psychological interpretation of an optimal time constant in tracking performance.

Studies of Optimal Ratios

In an early investigation, Sobczyk[68] studied aided tracking of an intermittent target on a radar display. The target was presented at flash rates of 1, 4, and 8 per second, while aiding-tracking ratios of 1, 2, and 3 seconds were tested. Constants of 2 to 3 seconds were found to be optimal. When different ratios of handwheel and cursor movement were tested, a significant interaction was found between aiding constant and handwheel ratio.

In another type of analysis, Phillips[50] described the tracker as a linear detector who turns his handwheel at a rate directly proportional to the perceived error. He then deduced that the operator's reaction time in perceiving and reacting to the error is 0.5 second, and theorized that the optimal aided-tracking time constant is a multiple of the reaction time. Phillips concluded that the optimal ratio is 2.5 seconds, a value that agrees with Sobczyk's results.

Near the end of World War II, the Foxboro Company[22] reported a study on aided tracking in which both handwheel and handlebar controls were used to adjust an indicator in following a target course. The target moved in only one direction, with a speed variation of 40 per cent. Aided-tracking ratios between 0 and 4.5 seconds were used, and 0.3 second was found to be optimal for both types of control devices and all conditions of acceleration. However, this study confirmed Sobczyk's findings showing an interaction between the handwheel-cursor ratio and the time constant, indicating again that there is no invariable optimal aided-tracking constant.

Intermittency Hypothesis

Notwithstanding the general lack of agreement among investigators as to the value of optimal time constants, there is a persistent belief among many engineers and psychologists who have worked in the tracking field that there is a specific optimal constant of about 0.5 second that should be used in all tracking systems.[1] This belief has been fostered by a psychological theory of tracking behavior that interprets it as a series of discrete perceptual-motor adjustments.

The first systematic formulation of this theoretical position was made by Mechler, Russell, and Preston,[46] who concluded that the optimal time constant represents the reaction time of the operator in detecting and responding to successive positions of the cursor or indicator in the tracking task. They developed an equation for the aided-tracking time constant based on a task in which the target appeared intermittently at a fixed rate. They assumed that if the tracker centered the cross hairs of an indicator

on the target each time it appeared, perfect tracking could be achieved when the interval between target appearances equaled the optimal aiding time constant. Thus, they derived the constant by determining the target rate that could be tracked most accurately. Then they went on to assume that an aiding constant arrived at by this method, because it eliminates transient reactions, is probably best for other types of target courses. The optimal constant indicated by their analysis was 0.5 second.

An analysis of tracking behavior similar to this reaction time hypothesis was formulated by Searle.[52] According to his intermittency hypothesis, the human operator in a tracking task responds to the perception of continuously generated error by making discrete corrections at a fixed frequency of about two per second. He assumed that a target moving in either a constant or a variable course generates in the humanly operated tracking system a nearly constant acceleration error, and that the tracker's errors of position and velocity are generated as dependent responses of this constant acceleration error.

Attempting to evaluate this hypothesis, Searle set up a tracking task in which the operator adjusted a joy stick, as on a small plane, to compensate for movement of a dot wandering horizontally from the center of an oscilloscope screen. Both acceleration aiding, i.e., automation of acceleration control, and rate aiding were studied. Optimal conditions of handwheel control were arranged prior to the experiment. The optimal aided-tracking time constant for rate aiding was found to be 0.5 second, a value that agrees with some of the earlier studies of the Foxboro Company and of Mechler, Russell, and Preston.

The common feature of these two psychological analyses of the optimal time constant is that they describe tracking behavior as a series of discrete alignment reactions to the continuously generated error in the target-cursor display. The time interval between reactions is considered a built-in "psychological delay," occasioned by the discrete perceptions of error and the responses of adjustment. This concept of intermittent "look-and-move" tracking performance is diagrammed in Figure 2-3. The "reaction time" between responses is arbitrarily equated to the operationally determined optimal time constant of 0.5 second. It should be noted in passing that this figure seems unreasonably high compared with generally accepted values for visual reaction time. One might expect a reaction time of the order of 0.5 second if the target course were completely erratic, but a significantly shorter time for a continuously moving target. Our own view, which we shall elaborate later, is that the reaction-time or intermittency hypothesis of tracking behavior is not valid, and that the so-called optimal time constant has little if anything to do with psychological reaction time.

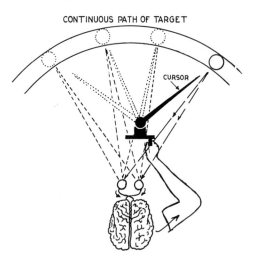

CONTINUOUS PATH OF TARGET

CURSOR

Figure 2-3. The intermittency hypothesis of tracking performance. According to this "look-and-move" description, tracking is made up of discrete perceptual-motor reactions separated by the reaction time necessary to respond to perceived error.

AIDED VERSUS DIRECT TRACKING

The unquestioning acceptance by most psychologists and engineers in the tracking field of the superiority of aided over direct tracking, and their preoccupation with the optimal time constant have all but obscured the more basic theoretical problem as to whether aiding devices are, in fact, aids or hindrances to the tracker. Aided tracking is a technological development that has had but limited justification from the behavior laboratory. The fact that it is clearly an improvement over velocity tracking is accepted as demonstrating its general superiority. The validity of the concept of aiding in tracking systems was hardly questioned for some years after World War II, until Lincoln and Smith[44] pointed out that any automation of the steering function introduces delays into the feedback control mechanism and reduces accuracy of the tracker.

Studies of Relative Accuracy of Different Types of Tracking

Some of the first comparative data on direct and aided tracking were obtained incidentally by Sobczyk,[68] who was studying tracking performance with an intermittently presented target. With one presentation of the target per second, aided tracking was superior to direct tracking. In a later study, Gebhard[26] compared direct and aided tracking of a target that appeared periodically on a radar scope and swept across the field. This type of situation, involving a unidirectional target course and uniform velocity, would seem to favor aided tracking. However, no significant differences were found between aided and direct tracking after the operator got on target and was tracking accurately.

VALIDITY OF AIDING QUESTIONED. As a result of many experiences of one of the authors in operating aided-tracking devices on Navy and Airforce gear in World War II, the point of view was developed that partial automation of the tracking task by rate aiding will rarely improve performance, and in general will decrease accuracy compared with direct pursuit tracking. This view was tested experimentally by Lincoln and Smith, who carried out a systematic comparison of direct, aided, and velocity tracking and attempted to define conditions of maximal performance for each type of system.

The apparatus used in this experiment has already been described (Fig. 2-1). The tracker's task was to follow a target moving in an oscillating circular path by adjusting a line cursor. This variable, oscillating course, in which the target reversed direction nine times, was very different from the unidirectional targets of uniform velocity that had been used by Sobczyk and Gebhard. Lincoln and Smith's apparatus provided quantitative variation and experimental control of all the significant factors of motor response and visual presentation involved in direct, aided, and velocity tracking. Several control studies were made to determine the optimal handwheel and cursor displacement ratios for the different conditions of tracking.

In the main part of the experiment, three experimental groups of 18 inexperienced subjects each, practiced tracking for approximately 30 minutes per day, for six days. One group performed direct pursuit tracking, another, aided tracking, and the third, velocity tracking. The mean accuracy scores of the three groups plotted over the six days are shown in Figure 2-4. The results are very clear-cut. Velocity tracking was very poor in relation to both the others, but direct pursuit tracking was consistently more accurate than aided tracking. Aided tracking showed more improvement due to learning than direct tracking, but never reached as high a level of accuracy.

THE "QUICKENING" DIVERSION. The clear demonstration by Lincoln and

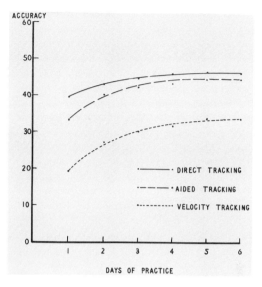

Figure 2-4. Accuracy in different types of tracking as a function of practice.

Smith of the superiority of direct over aided tracking was largely ignored by tracking psychologists and engineers for a number of years. Some aspects of the study were repeated by Birmingham, Kahn, and Taylor,[4] who curiously confined their comparative observations to velocity and aided tracking. Their confirmation of the superiority of aided over velocity tracking was nothing new; it was to achieve this improvement that aiding devices had been developed in the first place.

Although their experimental designs and experimental results offered no innovations, this group of Navy psychologists[4, 5] added a gloss of originality to their analysis by providing a whole new terminology for the persisting problems of aided tracking. They described the addition of an aiding control to a velocity tracking system as a process of "quickening." Thus, a velocity system is said to be an "unquickened" system, and an aided system is "quickened."

Birmingham and Taylor[5] stated that when rate control information of an aided display is added to a system in proper proportions, the operator achieves immediate knowledge of results of his control of the system. This statement is true only in the limited sense that the operator presumably can make a rational judgment of the automated rate of cursor movement produced by his positioning movement of the handwheel, in terms of the aiding time constant. No operator can "see" a generated rate immediately in terms of visual feedback signals. Yet this unwarranted assumption about the psychological effects of aiding (quickening) was accepted uncritically by many, while the basic problem of whether quickening can improve tracking performance to the level of direct tracking accuracy was deferred.

When an experimental comparison of direct and aided tracking was subsequently carried out by Chernikoff, Birmingham, and Taylor,[13] their results in general confirmed our earlier finding that direct tracking is superior. Accepting this situation reluctantly as "quite unusual and unexpected," they sought to define conditions in which quickened systems would be equal or superior to direct control. One effort in this direction was a comparison of direct with aided tracking for what is called a compensatory display of the target. In a compensatory display, target movement is indicated by variations of a spot or line from some reference or zero position on the display. As long as the target is being tracked accurately, there is no movement of the indicator from the reference position. When the indicator deviates from this zero position, the operator must adjust his control to compensate for the deviation.

Chernikoff, Birmingham, and Taylor found no significant differences between unaided and aided compensatory tracking, and accepted this finding as vindication of the use of quickened systems. From a practical point of view, however, this experiment has little value, for aiding mechanisms are not usually incor-

porated into compensatory tracking systems. And from a theoretical point of view, the experiment is ambiguous. There is evidence to show that compensatory tracking is quite a different problem, behaviorally, from pursuit tracking. In compensatory tracking, the tracker does not see target movement directly, but sees only error in tracking, in terms of deviations of the indicator from the zero position. When he sees a deviation of the indicator, he cannot know certainly whether it is due to some change in target movement or to his own control movements. These limitations in feedback, perhaps combined with other factors, make compensatory tracking in general inferior to pursuit tracking. This observation has been confirmed experimentally by Conklin.[15]

RELATIVE ACCURACY OF TRACKING SYSTEMS. The conclusion to be drawn from these various objective comparisons of different tracking systems is quite clear. Direct pursuit and aided tracking are both far superior to velocity control, which is still used in some Navy gear. Direct pursuit tracking is almost always superior to aided tracking, except in certain very limited conditions when the target is presented intermittently, or slowly and regularly in a straight line. Even under these special conditions, aided tracking may be no better than direct tracking, or may have but a slight advantage. The introduction of the quickening concept and the claimed superiority of quickened systems over unquickened is nothing more than a reaffirmation of the very poor performance status of velocity tracking. Quickened systems are still generally inferior to direct pursuit tracking. We believe that the psychological interpretation of these differences in tracking performance should be based on an understanding of the significance of delayed sensory feedback in these visually monitored behavior patterns.

SENSORY FEEDBACK THEORY OF TRACKING

Several theoretical formulations of the nature of tracking behavior have been proposed. One of these we have already mentioned—the reaction-time or intermittency theory, which describes tracking as a series of discrete responses with a built-in delay between responses. Another general response theory is couched in the language of learning and reinforcement psychology.[4, 5, 21] The sequentially linked responses of tracking are assumed to be organized and learned by means of reinforcement through knowledge of results. Delayed feedback would be delayed knowledge of results. A description of tracking in engineering terms is that the tracker is a part of a closed-loop servo mechanism who responds in a linear but discrete way to the continuously generated error between target and cursor.[36]

These descriptions of tracking have a common weakness in that they oversimplify the nature of tracking performance. Our own view is that tracking involves not a series of equivalent responses, but a highly organized, precisely coordinated motion pattern made up of at least two main movement components—manipulative or positioning movements, and transport or rate-control movements. Tracking motions are space-structured, relative to target movement, and their accuracy depends on continuous visual feedback signals from the target-cursor display. Any discrepancy between target and cursor is recorded by the feedback control mechanism, and leads to an immediate adjustment on the part of the tracker. The small positioning movements must be integrated with the larger rate-control movements, so that the precision of tracking depends on regulation of two kinds of movements by their own sensory feedback mechanisms, and the smooth integration of the two into a well organized tracking motion.

The critical feature of this theory is its conceptualization of the sensory feedback regulation of organized motion, in this case the visually monitored eye and hand motions of tracking. We do not conceive of tracking as composed of sequentially linked perceptions and responses, with measurable delays between responses. Rather we believe that the rate-control movements of tracking are effected by an uninterrupted pattern of muscular responses, regulated by a continuous barrage of afferent visual impulses from the target-cursor display. The feedback control mechanisms are sensitive to minute differences between target and cursor, and constantly monitor the speed and direction of rate-control movements. Superimposed upon these sweeping movements of eye and hand are the more discrete, manipulative positioning movements, which serve to realign cursor with target or reverse directions.

Within this theoretical framework, we assume that any delay of visual feedback signals to the tracker will decrease his tracking accuracy. The rate-control movements depend for their precision on immediate visual information of how well the movement is conforming to the environmental space pattern. Any delay beyond the normal light transmission time from the target display to the eyes of the tracker will interrupt this normal regulatory mechanism, and, with significant delays, the smoothly executed sweeping transport movements will tend to degenerate into discrete movements of decreased accuracy. The finer manipulative movements of tracking, which are naturally of a more discrete nature, will be affected somewhat differently by delayed feedback. Because these movements are of relatively high frequency, any delay in visual feedback tends to obscure the perceptual information of their effect and thus reduce their accuracy.

There are a number of fundamental differences between sensory feedback theory of tracking and the other descriptions that we have outlined above—the reaction-time, intermittency, reinforcement, and mathematical analyses. These other theories assume that movements of tracking are discrete, essentially equivalent in nature, i.e., unidimensional, and invariable with different conditions of target speed, delay, aiding, and so forth. They assume that there is a built-in delay in tracking, due to reaction time, perception time, or reinforcement time, so that the delay occasioned by aiding devices would help rather than hinder the tracker as long as the aided-tracking time constant is properly adjusted. They are inclined to equate the human tracking operator with machine systems, and to try to represent his responses as simple mathematical functions.

In contrast, sensory feedback theory asserts that tracking motions are multidimensional, that the rate-control component is not discrete but continuous. Further, different conditions of target speed, delay, aiding, and so forth would affect the tracking components differently, so that the overall integrated motion pattern would vary with changes in these conditions. Because delayed sensory feedback interrupts the normal regulatory mechanisms, any delay would be detrimental to accuracy except under the most limited conditions of target presentation that do not demand the flexibility of motion control characteristic of human behavior. Finally, we believe that no machine analogy or mathematical analysis yet devised can represent the response patterns of a behaving organism, and that the only valid analysis of tracking must be based firmly on a meaningful interpretation of the sensori-neuro-motor regulatory mechanisms of human behavior.

Many of these theoretical differences can be assessed specifically by experimental analysis. In the remainder of this section, we shall point out to what extent varied theoretical predictions are borne out by experimental results.

Transfer of Training Between Different Types of Tracking

For those who interpret tracking performance in terms of learning theory, the feedback effect of perceiving the target-cursor display is represented as knowledge of results, which serves to reinforce correct responses and to eliminate incorrect ones. This learning-reinforcement description assumes that tracking performances in direct, velocity, and aided tracking are very much the same, with only the time interval varying between response and reinforcement. Thus, with similar performances being learned, one would expect a great deal of positive transfer in learning between any two of the different types of tracking. In contrast, the sensory feedback theory would predict unequal transfer effects from one type of tracking to another because of the different performance patterns being learned. Because direct pursuit tracking is more efficient from the start, improves little with practice, and has none of the elements of delay that characterize aided and velocity tracking, we would expect less transfer between direct tracking and either of the other two than between aided and velocity tracking.

The original study on this transfer problem between direct and delayed systems was carried out by Lincoln,[42, 43] whose results are summarized in Figure 2-5. In this graph, direct tracking performance is represented in the first set of bars, aided tracking in the second, and velocity tracking in the third. In each case, the base line for the bars represents the accuracy level achieved by a training group in that type of tracking on the first day of practice. It can be seen that the initial accuracy for direct tracking is higher than for aided, and both are considerably higher than for velocity. The bars represent performance of transfer groups, that were tested in a particular type of tracking after six days of training in that or another type of tracking.

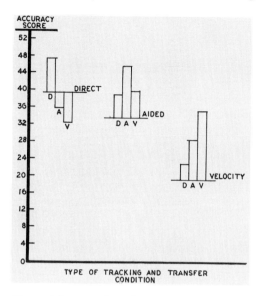

Figure 2-5. Transfer effects between different types of tracking. Base lines indicate initial accuracy of practice groups, and bars indicate performance of transfer groups, showing either positive (above base) or negative (below base) transfer effects. Initials D (direct), A (aided), and V (velocity) indicate original training of transfer groups. (Based on Lincoln.[42, 43])

The letters D, A, and V below the bars indicate the type of training of that particular group: direct, aided, or velocity. For each type of tracking, there is a bar showing performance of a group that had trained in that same type. These high bars represent approximately maximal performance accuracy for each type.

Examination of this bar graph shows that there was relatively little transfer from direct to velocity tracking, somewhat more from direct to aided. There was negative transfer from both aided and velocity to direct. That is, training in either of the delayed systems actually interfered with initial performance in direct pursuit tracking. Transfer from aided to velocity, and from velocity to aided was roughly equivalent. In each case, training in one type enabled the subjects to transfer to the other at a level about halfway between initial and maximal accuracy.

Holland and Henson[28] repeated some aspects of this work by studying transfer between quickened and unquickened acceleration controls in compensatory tracking. Their results confirm those of Lincoln with respect to the amount of transfer between aided and velocity tracking. In general, these differential transfer effects confirm our belief that movement organization in direct tracking is different from that in either aided or velocity tracking, with direct and aided more alike than direct and velocity.

Differential Analysis of Tracking Components

Except for the performance conceptions of Conklin,[14, 15] our own theory of tracking is the only one that emphasizes its multidimensional nature, in contrast to other theories that assume that all tracking responses are equivalent. A clear demonstration that there are multiple movement components in a tracking motion was provided by a study that analyzed changes in the pattern of tracking performance with variations in target speed.[44]

The hypothesis in this study was that there are two movement components in tracking—positioning movements and rate-control movements—and that the positioning movements would vary more in frequency as a function of learning than the rate-control travel movements, which depend more on the immediate visual feedback for their control. The procedure of the study was to obtain learning records of direct pursuit tracking at three different target speeds, designated slow, medium, and fast. These conditions corresponded roughly to tracking a rapidly moving ship, a small airplane at a distance of some two miles, and a high speed plane at the same distance. From the graphic records of tracking, the frequencies of movements of three different magnitudes were determined, of 1 mm., 1-3 mm., and 3-5 mm. wavelength.

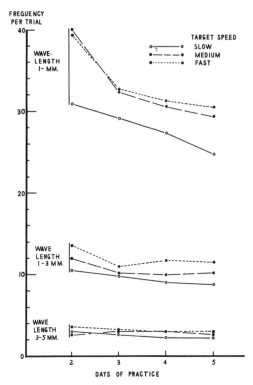

Figure 2-6. Frequency of error responses of different magnitudes in direct tracking for different target speeds as a function of practice. Each trial lasted one minute.

The results of this study, plotted in Figure 2-6, show that the change in movement organization during learning of a direct pursuit tracking task is principally a matter of eliminating small positioning movements. There was practically no change in frequency of large corrective movements during five days of practice at any target speed, and very little change in frequency of small movements, especially at the faster target speeds.

Interpretation of the Optimal Time Constant

Although the work of Lincoln and Smith[44] had demonstrated the multidimensional nature of tracking as well as the superiority of direct over aided tracking, it did not explain away the problem

of the optimal time constant in aided tracking. Even if the reaction time or perception time interpretation of this constant were rejected, the fact still remained that with certain specified conditions of aided tracking, an optimal time constant for accurate tracking could usually be found, and that this constant more often than not had a value around 0.5 second. Any valid theory of tracking must account for this phenomenon. The problem for sensory feedback theory was to determine why an aided-tracking time constant of approximately 0.5 second allowed greater accuracy than a larger constant of, for example, 1 second, which more nearly approximates the condition of direct tracking.

Our first step in this analysis was to determine whether the relative accuracy of aided tracking with different time constants changed as a function of target speed.[48] Figure 2-7 plots the results of this experiment, showing the interaction between target speed and aided-tracking constant. Tracking accuracy with three different delay constants is plotted as a function of target speed. At the slowest speed, the variation in accuracy due to time constant was relatively slight, although both the 0.5 and 0.25 second constants were superior to the 1 second constant. At higher target speeds, per-

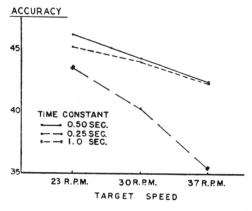

Figure 2-7. Tracking accuracy as a function of target speed with three different aided-tracking time constants.

formance was almost identical with constants of 0.5 and 0.25 second, but accuracy of tracking with a constant of 1 second dropped off sharply. In other words, the accuracy of aided tracking is a function not only of the time constant, but of target speed as well, and a so-called optimal constant is optimal only for certain conditions of the tracking task.

We believed that the significance of this interaction between delay constant and target speed lay in the change of movement organization with different conditions of tracking. Our wavelength analysis of the movements of direct tracking had shown that the small positioning movements accounted for most of the corrective adjustments, with intermediate movements and large rate-control movements occurring much less often. It is obvious that aided tracking, with its automated rate-control function, would require quite a different pattern of movements. Very few large movements are needed because of the generated velocity of the cursor; further, the very small positioning movements are at a minimum because their effect is obscured by the generated movement of the cursor. It seemed apparent that the aided-tracking motion pattern would be made up principally of movements of intermediate size, which would serve a dual purpose of correcting position and adjusting rate. We hypothesized that a wavelength analysis of the movements of aided tracking, with different time constants and different target speeds, would suggest why a certain constant would give optimal accuracy under given conditions.

In our study of the movement organization of aided tracking,[54] we analyzed graphic error records such as the one shown in Figure 2-8. We assumed that the shortest displacements of the tracking record were due to fine positioning and tremor movements, that the intermediate were due to interacting positioning and rate-control movements, and that the largest were due to rate-control or travel

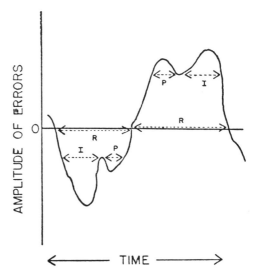

Figure 2-8. Part of a graphical record of tracking performance showing the method used to categorize error responses in terms of magnitude. R indicates rate-control; I, intermediate; and P, positioning errors.

movements. Prior to the experimental analysis, we predicted that there would be relatively more intermediate movements in aided tracking than we had observed in direct tracking, because of the nature of the task. We also predicted that increasing target speed would affect the frequency of occurrence of different types of movements much as in direct tracking. Finally, we predicted that increasing the value of the aiding constant (i.e., making the task more like direct tracking) would serve to increase the frequency of small positioning and large rate-control movements and to reduce the frequency of the intermediate or interacting positioning movements.

The graphs in Figure 2-9 and 2-10 show that all of these predictions were confirmed. Both of these graphs show that intermediate movements were more frequent than small or large. Figure 2-9 shows that the greatest change in frequency of movement with target speed was found for the small positioning movements, with practically no change

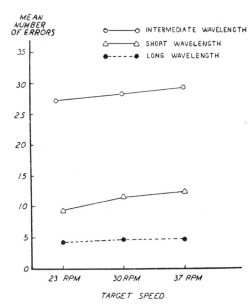

Figure 2-9. Frequency of error responses of different magnitudes in aided tracking as a function of target speed.

formance conditions being tested. There is no fixed optimal constant for all conditions, as was assumed by the reaction-time, perception-time, and reinforcement-time hypotheses; rather, the optimal constant varies with target speed, and probably with a number of other machine and performance variables.

This interpretation of the optimal time constant suggests that it represents a compromise between the positive effects of partial automation on rate control and the negative effects of this automation on positioning control. However, the fact that one can define an optimal arrangement for aided tracking does not mean that it is superior to direct tracking. The movement patterns of the two types of performance are so different that the optimal conditions for each must be determined independently. And, as the objective comparisons have shown, direct tracking is superior to aided tracking except under the most limited target conditions.

for rate-control movement—just as was found for direct tracking. The variation in frequency of different movement wavelengths as a function of aided-tracking time constant is shown in Figure 2-10. As predicted, the curves show that the intermediate positioning movements were reduced in frequency as the delay constant was increased in value, whereas the fine positioning and rate-control movements became more frequent.

The overall accuracy score of a tracking performance depends on an integrated record of movement errors of different magnitude. A frequency count of errors of different sizes, as we carried out in our wavelength analyses, does not indicate directly how large the integrated error will be. However, examination of Figure 2-10 suggests that as the very large and very small movement errors increase, and the intermediate movement errors decrease, there will be a point at which the integrated error will be smallest. This point will define the optimal aided-tracking time constant for the particular per-

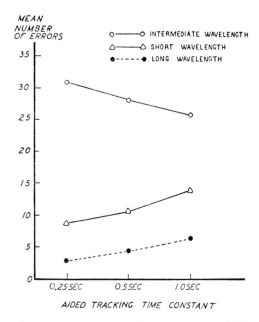

Figure 2-10. Frequency of error responses of different magnitudes with different aided-tracking time constants.

Specific Studies of Delayed Feedback

In the formulation of our sensory feedback theory of tracking, one of our basic assumptions has been that any delay in transmission of feedback signals to the tracker would be detrimental to his performance. In contrast, the other theories of tracking have accepted the delay inherent in aided tracking systems as a natural aspect of tracking performance. It is significant that whenever the effects of delayed feedback have been studied directly, the results have indicated that delay increased error.

The original studies of delayed visual feedback in tracking were more or less incidental observations on what was designated transmission lag in the presentation of error display to the tracker. In one of the Foxboro[22] studies of aided tracking, a procedure was tested which introduced a 0.1 second lag in the transmission of the visual display signals. The effect of this lag in aided tracking was to decrease accuracy slightly for all aided-tracking time constants used.

In a more extensive study, Warrick[77] introduced transmission lags into the error indication in a compensatory tracking task. This choice of task was unfortunate, in that compensatory tracking is naturally less accurate than pursuit tracking, as we have indicated above. It is difficult for the operator in compensatory tracking to differentiate between errors brought about by his own movements and those due to changes in target movement.

In this experiment, the operator used a knob control to recenter a pen-writer on an ink-writing oscillograph as the pen was made to deviate from its zero position in an irregular manner. Different time lags were produced by the ingenious method of masking the record with a device that had a viewing aperture cut into it, behind the moving pen. The interval between the operator's control movements and his perception of the effects of these movements could be varied by changing the distance between the viewing aperture and the writing point of the pen. Accuracy was recorded in terms of the time the pen remained within 1 mm. of the zero position.

The hypothesis being tested in the first phases of this study was that tracking accuracy would be a linear function of lag in error feedback. The results showed a progressive decrease in tracking accuracy as the lag increased from 0 to 320 milliseconds, but the function was not linear. Similar results were found for a regularly moving target course, with error lags of 0, 80, and 320 milliseconds. Warrick attempted to rationalize these results in terms of task difficulty, assuming that the lag function would be linear for a difficult target course, but would deviate more and more from linearity as the task became easier. This supposition was not confirmed in a further experiment, but no definitive interpretations were made.

Additional studies of delay in error feedback were carried out by Levine,[41] who found a linear relationship between the amount of lag and tracking accuracy. His results include observations of tracking when the error feedback was delayed from 0 to 2.7 seconds.

Conklin[14] carried out an extensive study involving partial lags of error indication from 0 to 16 seconds. When the target course had a coherent pattern, tracking accuracy dropped sharply with the shorter lags, and then tended to level off at a chance level of performance with delays of several seconds. When the target course was random, however, accuracy reduced to chance (and below!) with delays no longer than 1 second.

In a second study, Conklin[15] tested to what extent different control lags between 0 and 1 second, introduced in steps of 0.2 second, affected direct pursuit and compensatory tracking. Target courses of different complexity were used. Results showed that the function relating tracking accuracy and delay in error feedback was essentially linear in the range studied.

Comparing the relative effects of the lag on the two types of tracking, Conklin found that subjects learned to reduce error more with pursuit tracking than with compensatory. In fact, pursuit tracking with a 1 second display lag was better than compensatory tracking without any error delay. These results suggest that the deficiencies of compensatory tracking may result from intrinsic delayed sensory feedback factors in the compensatory display.

The general conclusion to be drawn from these various studies of transmission lag is that delayed visual feedback of motion is invariably detrimental to tracking performance. This is strong evidence for our assumption that the basic defect in velocity and aided tracking systems is the partial or selective feedback delay inherent in their operation.

The nature of the quantitative function between feedback delay and tracking accuracy is still in doubt, although it appears that this function is not consistently linear. The ambiguity in results probably arises from the fact that integrated error measures were used to assess performance. As we have shown, motion analysis of tracking performance reveals changes in movement organization with delays of different magnitude. Thus, it is not likely that a single quantitative function can describe the effects of delay on tracking performance.

Significance of Delayed Feedback in Organization of Tracking Motion

A meaningful interpretation of tracking behavior has a practical importance in the human engineering field, but also has far-reaching significance for theories of perceptual-motor integration. Although the precise organization of tracking motions is characteristic of human skill patterns, the sensori-neuromotor mechanisms underlying this organization have never been described adequately in psychology or physiology.

We believe that experimental analyses of tracking show clearly that these motion patterns are not primarily a phenomenon of learning, as assumed by Birmingham and Taylor[5] and others. In direct pursuit tracking, where the task conditions most nearly approximate what might be called the "normal" conditions of environmental control, relatively little learning improvement takes place. Compared with the more artificial conditions of velocity, aided, and compensatory tracking, direct pursuit tracking shows a high level of accuracy both initially and finally, with a minimal improvement due to practice. This indicates that the intrinsic organization of visually controlled skill patterns depends on integrative mechanisms that are standard equipment for the behaving organism. That is, the human system is built so that it can track moving stimuli with a high degree of precision; practice in a particular situation improves performance only moderately.

Motion analyses of tracking performance show that it is made up of two main component movements—transport or rate-control movements, and manipulative or positioning movements. It is our belief that failure to recognize this fact has resulted in oversimplified interpretations of tracking, which assume that it remains essentially the same type of response under all conditions. Changes in target speed and course, in perceptual display, and in feedback timing have differential effects on tracking movements that cannot be described adequately in single-factor terms.

Tracking movements are highly space-structured; that is, they can be made to conform precisely to the pattern of target movement. This precision depends primarily upon the continuous visual regulation of the rate-control movements of eye and hand. Positioning movements are discrete movements superimposed upon the continuous transport movements to correct for error. The assumption by Mechler, Russell, and Preston,[46]

Searle,[52] and Birmingham and Taylor that tracking movements are all alike, and all discrete, has not been confirmed.

The continuous visual regulation of tracking is achieved by means of sensory feedback mechanisms, which enable the tracker to register constantly the relative positions of target and cursor and to react immediately to differences in their positions. The "immediacy" is qualified only by the time of light transmission to the eye, and the time of neural transmission from sensory ending to the responding member. This interval is not of the order of magnitude of the so-called visual reaction time, nor should it be described in terms of a discrete perception of the display or of knowledge of results of one's movements. Sensory feedback control of motion implies that a difference in the visual display in itself initiates the corrective movement. Whether this difference is "perceived" is a matter of terminology; the important thing is that the sensori-neuromotor integrations of tracking are continuously monitored by means of visual feedback of the effects of one's own motion in relation to the target.

In a continuously monitored motion pattern, the introduction of any delay between the execution of a motion and the sensory feedback of its effects to the behaving individual tends to interrupt and change the intrinsic organization of the motion pattern and reduce its precision. There is ample evidence for this generalization in the delayed auditory feedback studies and the specific studies of delayed visual feedback, to be presented in the next three chapters. We have presented this extensive review of the problems of tracking because we believe that the only real problem here is one of feedback delay. Any machine system that interrupts and delays the normal feedback control of motion will be detrimental to motion efficiency. As long as we depend on human individuals to operate our tracking devices, we should take advantage of their built-in visual-motor precision, instead of reducing it by ill-conceived automation. So-called "aided" tracking has been a misnomer from the start, for it has been not an aid, but a hindrance to tracking precision.

SUMMARY

1. Delayed visual feedback is characteristic of machine systems that partially automate tracking or steering behavior. Practical problems related to such tracking devices have been studied since World War II.

2. The three basic types of tracking are direct pursuit, in which the operator has direct control of his cursor or indicator; velocity tracking, in which the operator's control generates a rate of movement of the cursor proportional to the magnitude of control movement; and aided tracking, in which a control movement positions the cursor directly, and also generates a rate of movement in it. Aided tracking is a great improvement over velocity tracking, and most tracking engineers have been convinced that aided tracking is also superior to direct.

3. The aided-tracking time constant is the ratio between the magnitude of a standard displacement of the cursor and the distance per second generated in the cursor by that displacement. To set this ratio for optimal tracking efficiency has been a design problem of aided tracking devices.

4. Although several investigators have found conflicting values for optimal time constants, it has been believed generally that there is one optimal ratio, of about 0.5 second, for all tracking conditions. This belief is related to theories that tracking behavior is a series of discrete responses, and that the optimal time constant represents the natural reaction time or perception time between responses.

5. The basic problem of tracking performance is whether aided tracking is

superior to direct pursuit tracking. Systematic comparisons of the two have shown that direct tracking is more accurate, except under some very limited conditions of intermittent target presentation, when aided tracking may be slightly better, or slow unidirectional target movement of uniform velocity, when neither aided nor direct tracking may have an advantage.

6. So-called "quickened" and "unquickened" tracking systems are equivalent to aided and velocity systems. The assumption that "quickening" eliminates the delay from informational feedback to the operator and makes quickened tracking superior to direct tracking is unfounded.

7. Sensory feedback theory describes tracking as a space-structured motion pattern made up of continuous rate-control movements, with discrete positioning movements superimposed. Rate-control movements are continuously monitored by visual feedback signals from the target-cursor display. Any delay in the feedback interrupts the integrative mechanism, and the continuous movements tend to break down into discrete movements.

8. Transfer of training between different types of tracking performance is not uniform, and not always positive. There is negative transfer from aided and velocity tracking to direct tracking. These differential effects indicate that learning theory of tracking performance is an oversimplification, for movement organization varies with different types of tracking.

9. Wavelength analyses of direct tracking movements over several days of practice show that the main change that occurs is the reduction in number of small, discrete positioning movements. Intermediate movements fall off slightly, but the number of large rate-control movements changes hardly at all. The relative frequency of small and intermediate movements is also dependent on target speed.

10. The relative advantage of different aided-tracking time constants depends on target speed, so that there is no one optimal constant. Wavelength analyses of aided-tracking movements show that movement organization of aided tracking is different from direct tracking, and changes with different values of the time constant. As the time constant is increased, small and large movements increase in number and intermediate movements decrease. These differential effects indicate that an optimal time constant represents the ratio, for given conditions of target presentation and other performance and machine variables, at which the integrated error record will be minimal.

11. Specific studies of transmission lag in error indication to the tracker show that such delay in feedback decreases accuracy. The quantitative delay function has sometimes been described as linear, but not consistently so, probably because of the multidimensional nature of tracking performance.

12. Tracking, along with other human skill patterns, is intrinsically organized by means of sensory feedback mechanisms of motion. Any delay of the feedback signals disturbs and changes the motion pattern, and reduces its precision. The defect in aided-tracking systems is the feedback delay that they introduce.

CHAPTER 3

DELAYED AUDITORY FEEDBACK

The feedback delay involved in tracking performance is a secondary effect introduced by the machine system that translates human motion into cursor motion. The tracker usually can see his own manual movements, but the effects of those movements are delayed in varying degrees. Because different tracking systems produce varying kinds of partially delayed feedback, the performance situation is not always clear-cut, and the quantitative effects of the different machine systems are not always comparable.

It is quite a different thing to introduce an experimental delay between the visual or auditory stimuli directly produced by an individual's movements and the transmission of those stimuli to his own eyes or ears. This is delayed sensory feedback in the strictest sense of the term, when the self-stimulation processes generated by motion are interrupted between the motion and the recording sensory endings. Systematic study of this type of feedback delay has awaited techniques by means of which the self-stimulation feedback processes could be controlled temporally. The first experiments of this nature, reported little more than a decade ago, were concerned with delayed auditory feedback of speech sounds. The first experiments on delayed visual feedback of motion have been even more recent.

The general method of delaying the auditory feedback of the sounds of speech (or other movement-generated sounds) is to record the sounds on magnetic tape, and then hold these sounds for a specified delay period by means of a tape loop. After traveling through the loop, the tape reaches a playback head that transmits the recorded sounds to the subject's ears by means of earphones. Besides its designation as delayed auditory feedback, this effect has been called delayed side-tone—referring to the fact that only air-conducted sound is delayed, and not bone-conducted—and also the "Lee effect," after the original investigator, who published the first report of delayed auditory feedback as a letter to the editor in 1950.[37]

LEE'S ORIGINAL EXPERIMENTS

Lee's[37-39] method of analysis of delayed auditory feedback is illustrated in Fig-

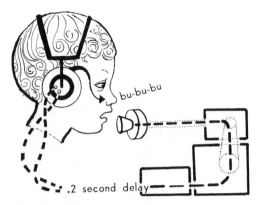

Figure 3-1. The technique of producing delayed auditory feedback.

ure 3-1. The subject's task was to speak into the microphone of a magnetic tape recorder that recorded the sounds of his voice. He wore sound-resistant earphones to prevent the normal air conduction of his speech sounds to his ears. The tape recorder was equipped with two heads, so that it could record and play back concurrently, and a tape loop device that carried the tape from the recording head to the playback head. The subject's speech sounds were recorded at one head, delayed for a fraction of a second by means of the tape loop, and played back to his ears via the earphones by the playback head. The magnitude of the delay interval, between speaking and auditory feedback, could be varied by adjusting the length of the tape loop.

Ordinarily, a speaking person stimulates himself to a certain extent by bone-conducted sound in addition to air-conducted sound. In the delayed feedback set-up, Lee adjusted the intensity of the played back delayed speech sounds to mask the immediate bone-conducted feedback, so that the subjects heard their own speech sounds somewhat louder than normal and a fraction of a second after uttering the sounds.

The most obvious effects of delaying the auditory feedback of the sounds of speech were a slowing down of speech, increased intensity and higher pitch, and

a serious disturbance of the speech pattern. Lee reported that a subject might stop completely, or, if he attempted to maintain normal speech rate with delayed feedback, would begin to stutter. This so-called artificial stutter consisted of repetitions of syllables, especially those with fricative sounds, such as *sh* and *ch*.

Quantitative Analysis

The five subjects used in Lee's principal experiment were required to read a passage of material containing 372 phonemes, with 65 spaces between words. Measures of total reading time were obtained under normal conditions and with three delay intervals, of 0.1, 0.2, and 0.3 second. In Figure 3-2, these time scores are plotted against magnitude of delay for each of the five subjects separately. The data show two types of performance with delayed speech feedback. Three subjects read progressively more slowly as the delay interval was increased from 0.1 to 0.3 second, but the other two subjects showed only slight decrease in reading rate.

Lee attempted to derive a predictive

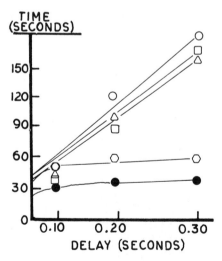

Figure 3-2. Total reading time as a function of magnitude of feedback delay, for five subjects. (Based on Lee.[38])

formula that would describe the effects of delayed feedback on reading time. His basic assumption was that the speaker functions as a machine, and that a single formula can be found to describe the effect of feedback delay on reading time. He proposed that: $T = n (d — t)$, where T equals reading time with delayed feedback; n, the number of units of speech plus the intervals between words; t, normal reading time; and d, the delay interval. This formula generally predicts a linear relationship between delay and reading time. As Lee's data show, such a relationship was found with some of the subjects, but not all.

Theoretical Analysis

Lee based his general theoretical analysis of the effects of delayed auditory feedback on certain assumptions about the neural and behavioral organization of the speech mechanism. As indicated in Figure 3-3, he described speech as a series of neural feedback loops, involved in the

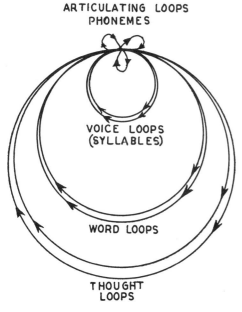

Figure 3-3. Model of the neural mechanisms of speech proposed by Lee. (Based on Lee.[38])

production of what he calls phonemes, syllables, words, and thought. These separate loops are arranged in a hierarchy of speech control, the different levels of which are related to articulation, voice, word production, and thinking. According to Lee, this model will explain normal speech, delayed speech feedback effects, motor aphasias, and natural and artificial stutters.

Lee went on to say that his theoretical model of speech is consistent with neuroanatomy. The model assumes that the speech mechanism is composed of loops at different levels with a common junction, presumably a center of the brain at which both volitional and reflex switching occurs. The length of each loop is roughly proportional to the time required to perform the particular speech activity—articulation, operation of the breath system for volume, tension of the vocal cords for pitch and inflection, and so on. The inner two sets of loops, labeled articulation and voice, represent the speech mechanism proper.

Lee proposed further that the hearing system is in series or inductively coupled to the voice loop for the aural monitoring function. Thus, the analysis of delayed speech feedback offers the most information for understanding the voice functions of the speech system. The other two loops, word production and thought, have more to do with speech habits.

According to Lee's analysis, the articulation loop and voice loop are monitored at the reflex level—the articulation of phonemes by tactile and kinesthetic means, and the voice loop by aural means. Any speech element at the level of the syllable may be repeated if the hearing monitor is not satisfied. When the monitor is satisfied, the signal ascends to the next loop and forms a part of the next larger component. Monitoring of the loops governing word production and thought is volitional, and involves decision-making in organizing speech patterns. The word loop also provides a device for stalling or maintaining the speech flow as a defense against interruption. This stalling mechanism gives a nervous quality to speech, which all speakers utilize more or less. When used excessively, such stalling represents what is called Class I stutter.

The aphasias, which include impairments in the ability to use abstract word concepts, in specific word usage, in the overall ability to speak, and varied combinations of these defects, result from malfunctioning throughout the four-loop system. The action of this system depends not only on the processes of somesthetic, aural, and volitional monitoring, but also on switching of signals within loops.

Lee based his interpretation of delayed speech feedback in part on the so-called artificial stutter induced by the delay. This stutter, he said, duplicates what is usually described as Class I or clonic stutter and involves voluntary repetition of syllables or words. In the case of feedback delay, the repetition is produced because the aural monitor of the voice loop is unsatisfied. The voice loop continues for one or two extra cycles of action until the arrival of the delayed feedback triggers the next process. The analysis of delayed speech feedback has no significance, however, in understanding tonic or Class II stutter, which is related to phoneme articulation and the action of the smallest loop. Thus, the technique of delayed speech is critical for studying the processes of the voice loop, but not for the articulation loop. Lee speculated that experimental intervention in the articulation loop would require techniques of the anesthetist or neuroanatomist.

This first theoretical analysis of delayed auditory feedback is distinctive in bringing the quantitative point of view to the problem. However, the theoretical model of the speech mechanism is itself speculative, and cannot be confirmed by either neural or behavioral analyses. Further, Lee's own experimental findings on the effects of delay do not necessarily require the sort of interpretation he advances. He offers no explanation for the individual differences in time data that were found for the different subjects. We believe that these different forms of adapting to feedback delay indicate that speech control is somewhat more flexible than Lee implies, and that aural monitoring is not necessarily a higher level of control than somesthetic monitoring. The subjects who performed most successfully under conditions of delayed auditory feedback were probably able to ignore, for the most part, the nonsynchronized sounds of speech and to control their speech mainly by means of somesthetic feedback signals.

ANALYSES OF SPECIFIC DELAY EFFECTS

A number of investigators have analyzed the effects of delayed speech feedback since Lee's[37] first report. The technique of delaying auditory signals has been similar in all cases, involving the use of magnetic tape recorder and playback heads. However, the later investigators have used many different performance measures and different methods of analysis.

Duration of Speech

As noted by Lee, one of the most obvious effects of delayed auditory feedback is a slowing down of speech, an effect which has been observed and measured by a number of investigators. In an experiment by Chase, Harvey, Standfast, Rapin, and Sutton,[9, 10] fourteen young adults were required to repeat the speech sound "b" in groups of three, first with nondelayed feedback through earphones and then with a delay of 0.24 second. The speech sounds were all recorded on a cathode-ray oscilloscope, and this visible

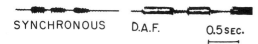

SYNCHRONOUS   D.A.F.   0.5 SEC.

Figure 3-4. Visible speech records of the repeated sound of "b" with synchronous feedback and delayed auditory feedback of 0.24 second. Both intensity and duration increased with delay. (From Chase, Harvey, Standfast, Rapin, and Sutton.[9])

display was then photographed. Figure 3-4 illustrates the type of recording obtained. With such records, the duration of specific sounds and the intervals between the grouped syllables could be measured directly and converted into time values.

In this experiment, there was a marked increase in the duration of the intersyllable interval when auditory feedback was delayed. The mean intersyllable interval for the 14 subjects with normal speech feedback was 0.35 second, with a range of 0.14 to 0.73 second. The mean intersyllable interval with delayed feedback was 0.56 second with a range of 0.17 to 1.97 seconds. This difference between means was statistically significant.

A comprehensive analysis of various effects on speech of different intervals of delayed auditory feedback was carried out by Fairbanks.[19] Sixteen young men read a passage made up of six sentences containing a total of 98 words under five auditory conditions, all employing amplified feedback. In the first condition, the feedback was nondelayed, and in the other four, delays of 0.1, 0.2, 0.4, and 0.8 second were used. Figure 3-5 plots sentence duration as a function of delay interval. There was marked reduction in reading rate with delays of 0.1, 0.2, and 0.4 second, with the maximal slowing at 0.2 second. Only limited slowing was observed with the 0.8 second delay interval.

Fairbanks described the increased duration of speech as a direct effect of delayed auditory feedback, along with articulatory disturbances that resulted in speaking errors. He proposed to combine

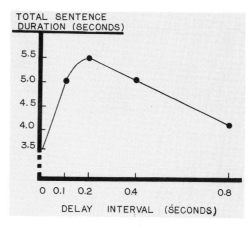

Figure 3-5. Duration of speech as a function of magnitude of feedback delay. (Based on Fairbanks.[19])

measures of these two effects into one—the correct word rate. Figure 3-6 shows his rate of speaking data for all words and for correct words expressed as relative values with the rates for nondelayed feedback equaling one. As shown by the

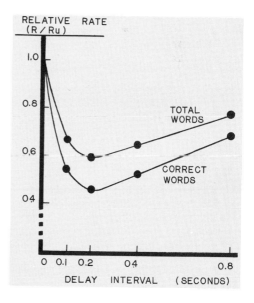

Figure 3-6. The relative rate of speaking computed from total words and total correct words as a function of magnitude of feedback delay. (Based on Fairbanks.[19])

curves, the rates for total words and for total correct words declined below the normal value as the delay interval increased to 0.2 second, and then showed a gradual rise. The two curves have similar shapes, and are clearly falling and rising functions. Thus, the word rate measures, as well as the duration measures, showed a maximal disturbance of delayed feedback at 0.2 second.

Other significant studies of the effects of delayed feedback on the duration of speech have been reported by Black,[6] Rawnsley and Harris,[51] Spilka,[69] and Tiffany and Hanley.[76] The latter found that the slowdown effect became more marked as the intensity of the delayed sound was raised. Spilka observed that while the effects of the delay on other measures of speech varied in relation to the type of reading materials used, the change in rate was much the same for all materials.

Intensity of Speaking

Another generally observed effect of feedback delay is an increase in intensity of the spoken sounds. Figure 3-7 shows this effect at different delay intervals as

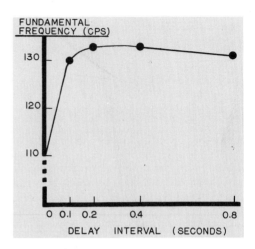

Figure 3-8. Fundamental pitch of speech as a function of magnitude of feedback delay. (Based on Fairbanks.[19])

observed by Fairbanks. The measured intensity of speech rose sharply with the shortest delay interval of 0.1 second, increased somewhat more with a 0.2-second delay, and remained high for all other delay intervals used. The peaking effect observed for the time measures was not found for the intensity changes.

Similar findings on changes in speech intensity were observed by Black, who found that subjects reading under conditions of delayed feedback spoke progressively louder as the magnitude of the delay was increased from 0 to 0.27 second. The intensity increases beyond delay values of 0.09 second were not statistically significant.

Fundamental Voice Frequency

Feedback delay causes increases in the fundamental frequency of the voice that are very similar to the intensity increases. Figure 3-8 shows this effect in terms of frequency increases in cps as a function of delay interval, as determined by Fairbanks. The curve is very similar to the one in Figure 3-7 for intensity increases, and may very well be influenced by the variation in intensity, inasmuch as an

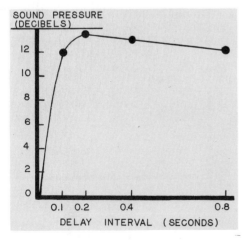

Figure 3-7. Intensity of speech as a function of magnitude of feedback delay. (Based on Fairbanks.[19])

increase in speaking intensity typically is accompanied by elevation of the pitch of the voice.

Errors in Speaking

All investigators of delayed auditory feedback have observed that it produces articulatory disturbances and speech errors of various types. Figure 3-9 illustrates Fairbanks' first observations on the incidence of articulatory errors with delays of different magnitude. The shape of this curve is comparable to that for speech duration, showing a maximal number of errors with a delay of 0.2 second and fewer with shorter and longer delays. Fairbanks considered the articulatory disturbance and the increase in speech duration as direct effects of the delay, and the intensity and pitch variations as indirect effects.

Fairbanks also compared the relative number of articulatory errors with the number of words that were misread, as shown in Figure 3-10. The relative number of articulatory errors was determined by dividing the number under each delay condition by the number made under normal conditions of speaking. The results show that the delay has far less

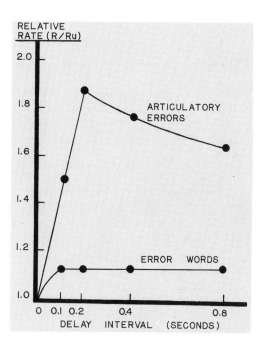

Figure 3-10. The relative number of articulatory errors and relative number of words misread as a function of magnitude of feedback delay. (Based on Fairbanks.[19])

effect on word organization than it has upon control of the articulatory movements involved in the formation of syllables.

In another systematic study, Fairbanks and Guttman[20] analyzed the articulatory disturbances produced by feedback delay in terms of the types of errors made in speaking. The 16 young men who were used as subjects read a prose passage of 55 words seven times in all. The first was a pre-experimental reading under normal conditions. The subjects wore earphones and spoke into the microphone for five experimental readings, for which feedback delays of 0, 0.1, 0.2, 0.4, and 0.8 second were used, and the sound intensity was amplified. Finally, a post-experimental reading was made under normal conditions. Tape recordings of the readings were available for analysis.

In order to measure articulatory accuracy, the correct word rate in words per

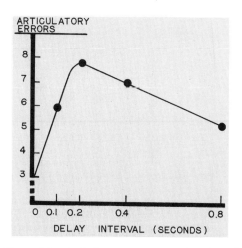

Figure 3-9. Articulatory errors as a function of magnitude of feedback delay. (Based on Fairbanks.[19])

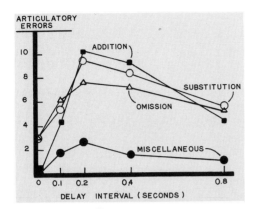

Figure 3-11. Incidence of different types of errors with feedback delays of different magnitudes. (Based on Fairbanks and Guttman.[20])

turbance at the longer delay intervals. The graph in Figure 3-11 shows the incidence of the various types of errors—substitution, omission, addition, and miscellaneous. Each curve peaks at 0.2 second and falls off thereafter. The curves for substitution, omission, and addition errors are very similar and may not vary significantly from each other.

Chase, Sutton, Rapin, Standfast and Harvey[12] carried out a similar quantitative analysis of correct word rate as a function of feedback delay, using six delay intervals from 0.138 to 0.394 second. Their results, summarized in the bar graph in Figure 3-12, in general confirm those of Fairbanks and Guttman. The number of correct words per second decreased and then increased as a function of delay magnitude. In this study, the delay interval that induced the most marked speech disturbance was 0.244 second.

second was calculated from the total number of correct words uttered and the total reading time. The errors in the speech record were then classified into errors of substitution, omission, addition, and miscellaneous errors. Substitution errors, which were described as involving improbable phonetic elements and monophonetic sounds, occurred in stressed syllables. Omission errors often involved several phonetic units of speech. Addition errors appeared to be "nonpurposeful" responses, and were almost always double articulations. Nonrepetitive additions were unstressed, and occurred between words. Two less common types of errors, classified miscellaneous, were described as slighting and shifted juncture.

All measures of speech performance obtained in this study—total correct words, reading duration, correct word rate, and number of errors, either total or classified—showed a marked variation with variation in the delay interval. Delayed speech feedback consistently caused decreases in total correct words and correct word rate, and increases in total reading time and number of errors. Here again a peak disturbance was found at 0.2 second, with declining levels of dis-

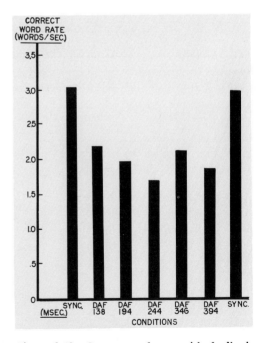

Figure 3-12. Correct word rate with feedback delays of different magnitudes. (From Chase, Sutton, Rapin, Standfast, and Harvey.[12])

Artificial Stutter

Investigators of delayed speech feedback have shown considerable interest in the repetitive speech errors made by subjects. Lee[39] described this effect as artificial stutter, and thought the effect was an analogue of oscillating feedback in electronic circuits.

In their analysis of speech errors, Fairbanks and Guttman found that about 70 per cent of the additive errors were repetitive, of the nature of a stutter. These repetitions were not corrective, as we see occasionally in normal speech, but were described as nonpurposeful, and seemed to be intrinsic reactions to determinative stimuli. Almost all these stutter-like repetitions were simple double articulations, and, more often than not, the repeated articulation was stressed rather than unstressed. According to Fairbanks and Guttman, both error and increased effort in speaking occurred at times of uncertain or precarious control of articulation, as governed by the delay period.

During some observations on his own speech under delay conditions, Chase[8] noted that, although he did not stutter as a result of the delay, once he started repeating syllables, he found it difficult to stop. He interpreted this effect to mean that delayed hearing facilitates the circulation of speech units in the auditory-speech feedback loop, and speculated that it might be possible to repeat a single speech sound more rapidly with delayed feedback than under control conditions. To test these ideas, Chase had subjects repeat the sound "b" as rapidly as possible during a 5-second control period without delay, and then for an equal period with a feedback delay of 0.22 second. Out of 20 subjects, 17 repeated the sound more frequently under the delay condition, two showed no difference in rate, and one repeated the sound more times during the control period.

Chase felt that this observed facilitative effect of delayed feedback on repetition rate was of significance relative to the artificial stutter induced by delay and also to actual stutter, and speculated as to the physical aspects of the speech signal that might regulate repetition and stutter in speech. Several possible conditions were suggested as determining the facilitative effect of delay: (a) changes in temporal relations of speech signals, (b) changes in physical aspects of speech signals themselves, and (c) changes in the acoustic environment around the speaker's ear.

Chase speculated further that delayed feedback would facilitate repetition only of speech units "smaller than a syllable," and that the speaker would hear this repetition as prolongation of the syllable. However, the best description of speech in terms of its movement components describes the syllable as the basic unit of speech, which cannot be subdivided further.[70] A syllable can be modified in various ways by articulatory movements, but no spoken articulation is "smaller than a syllable," for a spoken unit is a syllable. From this point of view, one can speculate that Chase's subjects achieved a faster repetition rate of spoken *b* sounds with delayed feedback because they were free of acoustic monitoring and probably allowed the spoken syllable to shift to a simpler pattern. That is, the subjects were instructed to repeat, "bee, bee, bee," and probably maintained this sound with normal feedback. With loss of auditory monitoring, the speech pattern may have changed to something like "buh, buh, buh," or even "puh, puh, puh"—syllables that can be repeated more rapidly than "bee."

Emotional Disturbances

Some of the most striking effects of delayed speech feedback are the emotional disturbances, frustration, and fatigue that result from sustained performance under these conditions. Lee[37] first observed that speaking against delayed sidetone for more than a few seconds produced marked emotional tension and frustration, fatigue, and reddening of the face. Hanley, Tiffany and Brungard[27] have studied the emotional effects specifically in relation to intensity of the delayed feedback, using skin resistance changes as a measure of emotional involvement. Fifty subjects were tested with five sound pressure levels of delayed sidetone. Both the latency of the skin-resistance change and the pattern of the recorded change were analyzed. It was found that both the latency and the pattern were directly related to the sound pressure level of the delayed sidetone. Judges examining the records were able to specify the intensity level used in specific observations from the recorded effects.

DEVELOPMENTAL ANALYSIS

Chase, Sutton, First, and Zubin[11] compared the effects of delayed speech feedback in children of different ages, from four to nine years. Each yearly group included eight to ten children, about evenly divided between boys and girls. The subjects were all from a summer camp, and had normal speech and hearing.

The procedure used was to ask each child to draw a person and then tell a story about him. Before the story was told, the child was fitted with a headset to which a microphone and earphones were attached. As the child told his first story, the auditory signals were led directly to the earphones, without delay but with some amplification. At the end of the story, the experimenter asked three questions: "Whose voice did you hear? Where was it coming from? Did you like the sound of it?" After the child answered, he was asked to tell another story about his drawing. For this second story, the standard magnetic tape tech-

nique was used to delay the auditory feedback. A delay interval of 0.2 second was used, and the auditory signal was amplified as before. The experimenter then asked the three original questions plus two more: "Did your voice sound different from before? What was different about it?"

Several measures of speech performance were obtained: number of words, excluding repetitions, in the speech sample; number of syllables; number of intrusions ("uh," "um"); total speech time, excluding pauses greater than six seconds; number of word repetitions; number of syllable repetitions; and number of syllables prolonged in time. Inasmuch as the speech samples varied in length, these raw scores were translated into ratio measures to control for total time of speaking. The measures thus obtained included word rate, percentage of words

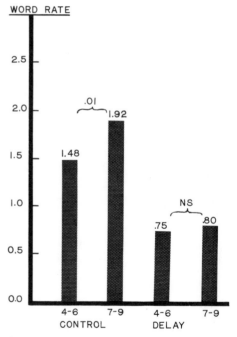

Figure 3-13. Word rate of two age groups of children with synchronous feedback (Control) and with feedback delay of 0.2 second. The age difference was significant with synchronous feedback, but not with delay. (Based on Chase, Sutton, First, and Zubin.[11])

repeated, percentage of syllables repeated, percentage of syllables prolonged, and percentage of intrusions. Nonparametric methods were used to assess the significance of differences.

To analyze the data, the children were divided into a younger group of 26 subjects, four to six years old, and an older group of 28 subjects, seven to nine years old. The differences between groups were compared for both the control and delay conditions. Figure 3-13 represents the comparative means for the word rate measure. Here it can be seen that the younger children had a significantly lower word rate during the control condition, but the difference between the groups during delayed feedback was not significant. Both groups slowed their rate markedly with delayed speech, but the older group slowed relatively more. Figure 3-14 shows the comparative data for percentage of syllables prolonged. During the control condition, the younger group had a slightly higher score which

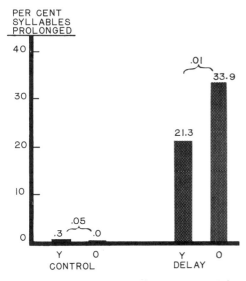

PER CENT SYLLABLES PROLONGED

Figure 3-14. Per cent of syllables prolonged for two age groups of children with synchronous feedback (Control) and with feedback delay of 0.2 second. The age difference was significant at 5 per cent with synchronous feedback, and at 1 per cent with delay. (Based on Chase, Sutton, First, and Zubin.[11])

was significant at the 5 per cent level. With delayed feedback, the scores for both groups increased remarkably, but now the older group showed a much higher score, significant at the 1 per cent level. The other measures obtained—percentage of intrusions, percentage of words repeated, and percentage of syllables repeated—showed a very low incidence in both age groups and under both control and delay conditions. What differences were observed in these measures in relation to age were not significant.

The data in Figures 3-13 and 3-14 indicate that the older children of seven to nine years were affected more by delayed speech feedback than the four to six year old children. The older children showed a greater decrease in word rate, and a larger increase in percentage of syllables prolonged.

Analysis of the children's answers to the questions showed some differences related to age. Older children invariably identified their voice as their own in both the control and the delayed feedback conditions; in contrast, about half of the younger children gave various other identifications of their voice under both conditions. Almost all of the older children localized the sound in the earphones, while almost a third of the younger group localized it in the microphone or elsewhere. Over three-fourths of the younger children liked the sounds heard, whether delayed or not, but only about half of the older children liked the delayed speech. Although almost all of the children recognized some difference in the delayed speech, none of the younger group identified the difference in terms of time, whereas almost half of the older children made some reference to a time difference.

The results of this one study indicate that younger children are less severely affected by delayed speech than older children. This difference is probably a developmental effect, related to the increasing degree of control of the speech mechanism during childhood. The speech of young children is less precise than that of older children, and conforms less well to auditory patterns. Children in general show increasing ability to carry a tune and duplicate musical rhythms throughout their early years in school. It seems logical to assume that as auditory control of vocal activities becomes more precise, the disturbance from delayed auditory feedback should become correspondingly more severe.

ADAPTATION TO DELAYED HEARING

There have been observations on two types of adaptation to delayed hearing, i.e., adjustment within a single period of exposure, and changes in mode of response to the delayed feedback with repeated exposures.

Observations on adjustments within a single period were first reported by Atkinson,[2] who investigated reading performance during a five-minute period of delayed feedback, using delay intervals from 0.03 to 0.3 second. Subjects showed the usual slowing of speech under delay conditions, as well as increased intensity. No real evidence of improvement in reading during the course of the exposure was found. Neither reading rate nor sound pressure level changed significantly during the five minutes. However, Atkinson did not rule out the possibility of adaptation with longer periods of performance.

Adaptation with Repeated Exposures

Tiffany and Hanley[76] studied the adaptation of 20 subjects to delayed speech feedback over a series of 24 readings during two weeks. The task was to read a 45-word prose passage with a feedback delay of 0.18 second. Measures of reading time and reading fluency were obtained.

The results showed no significant adaptation in reading rate over the interval studied, but there was significant adaptation in terms of fluency. Readers learned to avoid repetitions and omissions of words, syllables, and sounds. However, the adaptation phenomena were by no means consistent. Some subjects became markedly worse over the series of readings, while others showed improvement.

During the first series of 12 readings, it was observed that there was a negative correlation between reading ability and rate adaptation. That is, the better readers appeared to be unable to overcome the rate effects as well as the poorer readers. No such correlation was found for the fluency measures.

In another study of adaptation, Winchester, Gibbons, and Krebs[78] found significant decrease in reading time after the first two reading periods. Their results, showing reading duration for ten periods of reading prose with auditory delay, are plotted in Figure 3-15. Al-

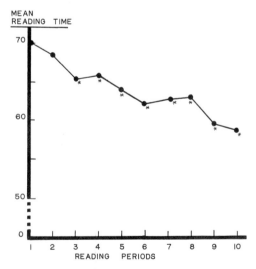

Figure 3-15. Mean reading time in ten successive test periods with delayed auditory feedback. The first period mean was significantly different at the 1 per cent level from the third through tenth period means. (Based on Winchester, Gibbons, and Krebs.[78])

though the difference between the first and second periods was not statistically significant, the differences between the first period and the third through tenth periods were significant beyond the 1 per cent level. Reading time decreased 16 per cent from the first to the tenth test periods. This indication of significant adaptation in reading rate to delayed speech feedback differs from Tiffany and Hanley's negative finding.

Persisting Aftereffects

In an early study, Black[6] observed that the decreased rate of reading resulting from delayed speech feedback of 0.18 second persisted to some extent for reading done immediately after the exposure period. He later planned a study to measure these aftereffects.[7] An experimental and a control group, each composed of 28 subjects, read 10 lists of 5-syllable phrases. The phrases were read at 5-second intervals, while the duration and relative sound pressure level of each phrase were recorded. The control group read all 10 lists with no delay. For the experimental group, a delay of 0.3 second was introduced during the reading of Lists 3 and 4, and then discontinued with no warning to the subjects.

Because analyses of variance showed significant variation in performance relative to the successive lists of phrases read by the subjects, the performance of the experimental group was compared with that of the control group for each successive list to test for the effects of the delay and aftereffects. When the delay was introduced, the experimental group showed a significant increase in sound pressure and a highly significant increase in reading time, measured in duration per phrase. When the delay was discontinued, there was no longer a significant difference in sound pressure. Relative to reading rate, the experimental group was still significantly retarded over the control group in List 5, and never achieved

as fast a rate throughout the course of the experiment, although the differences for Lists 6 through 10 were not statistically significant. The author concluded that reading rate continued to be affected for at least 150 seconds after the delay had been discontinued.

Tiffany and Hanley reported observations on aftereffects of delayed speech feedback at the conclusion of their two-weeks' study. There were some aftereffects of the periodic exposure to delayed speech, and these effects appeared to be related to the degree that the speaker had been disturbed during the delay period. Readers who were greatly disturbed by the feedback delay read more slowly in the post-exposure performance, whereas readers who were disturbed only in limited ways tended to increase their reading rate in the post-exposure period.

DELAYED HEARING AND NONVOCAL ACTIVITIES

Although most of the observations on delayed auditory feedback have been concerned with the effects on speech, similar effects have been reported with other sound-producing movement patterns. Lee[37] early observed that a skilled wireless telegraph operator was incapable of rhythmic tapping while listening to his signaling on a delay circuit. He sent the wrong pattern of dots and dashes for well known letters. Lee also asked a skilled tympanist to perform with delayed auditory feedback, and observed that his performance was erratic with little or no rhythm.

Kalmus, Denes, and Fry[30] carried out a controlled experiment on the effects of delayed hearing on rhythmic handclapping. A metronome was used to click at 2-second intervals, to signal the start of a task. Subjects were asked to perform two tasks. In the first, they clapped their

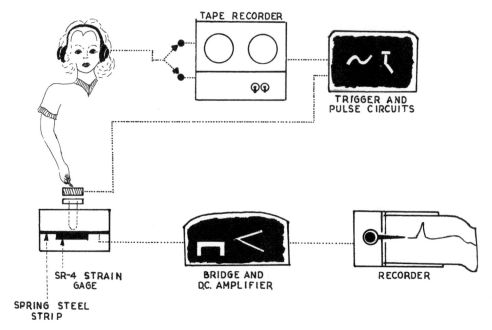

Figure 3-16. Technique of delaying the auditory feedback from nonvocal activity (tapping). (Based on Chase, Sutton, Rapin, Standfast, and Harvey.[12])

hands regularly six times after the click, and in the second, they clapped two groups of three beats each after each click, with a strong accent on the first clap of each group. The metronome sound was never delayed, but the auditory feedback from the handclapping was delayed 0.25 second for the experimental trials.

With the delayed feedback, the rhythm of handclapping was almost invariably disrupted. In the first task, subjects often clapped seven times instead of six, and at other times ceased clapping altogether after alternate clicks. In the second task, subjects almost always clapped four times instead of three in the second group, and were often unaware of their mistakes. Subjects who recognized their errors could sometimes overcome them by concentrating and slowing down their performance.

In another systematic analysis, Chase, Harvey, Standfast, Rapin, and Sutton[9, 10] compared the effects of delayed hearing on speech and key tapping. Their tech-

nique of recording and delaying the auditory feedback from the nonvocal activity is shown in Figure 3-16. When the subject tapped upon a key, the pressure was recorded by a strain gauge that transmitted an electrical signal to an amplifier for recording on an oscillograph. The sound from the key as it hit the spring steel to which the strain gauge was attached was recorded by a microphone and then played back to the subject's ear with amplification.

Fourteen young men served as subjects. They were asked to repeat the sound *b* in groups of three until seven to ten such groups had been uttered. Their second task was to tap the key in a similar manner, i.e., in groups of three taps for seven to ten groups. These procedures were carried out under normal control conditions and again with an auditory feedback delay of 0.244 second.

Records obtained in this study are shown in Figure 3-17. This figure indicates the relative intensity and duration of key tapping and speech movements

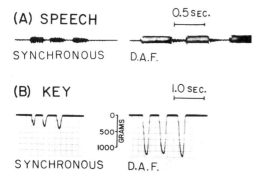

(A) SPEECH

0.5 SEC.

SYNCHRONOUS   D.A.F.

(B) KEY

1.0 SEC.

SYNCHRONOUS   D.A.F.

Figure 3-17. Oscillographic records of the repeated sound of "b" and repeated taps with synchronous feedback and delayed auditory feedback. Both intensity and duration increased with delay. (From Chase, Harvey, Standfast, Rapin, and Sutton.[9])

with normal synchronous conditions and with auditory delay. The effect of the delayed hearing was to increase the intensity, duration, and intermovement interval of both types of movements. Figure 3-18 summarizes the quantitative differences between the control (C) and delay (D) conditions. The bar graphs show increases in both intensity (plotted in arbitrary units) and time between movements comparable in magnitude for key tapping and speech. These differences between the control and delay conditions indicated here were all statistically significant.

It is evident from these limited investigations of nonvocal activities that feedback delay produces comparable effects on quite different motion patterns. Apparently the temporal pattern of sensory feedback is of general significance in the organization of behavior, for the disturbing effects of feedback delay are not confined to specific motion patterns such as speech.

ACCELERATED AUDITORY FEEDBACK

Inasmuch as the normal auditory feed-

back of speech is mainly airborne sound, it is somewhat slower in reaching the ear than electronically conducted sound. Thus, it is possible to accelerate the feedback time of speech sounds to a speaker's ears over the normal transmission time. The original experiment on accelerated speech feedback was designed by Peters,[49] who compared reading rates with normal feedback time of 0.001 second with rates when the auditory feedback was accelerated to intervals of 0.0003 second (equivalent to bone-conducted feedback) and 0.00015 second. The subjects, who were instructed to read naturally, read progressively faster as the feedback time was decreased. The differences were slight but consistent. This study also demonstrated consistent variations in reading rate related to changes in the sound pressure level of the feedback. Speakers read progressively faster as the feedback intensity was decreased. Figure 3-19 illustrates the measured variations in reading duration relative to both speed and intensity of the auditory feedback for one set of phrases read by the subjects. Although not all of the differences between means were statistically significant, the

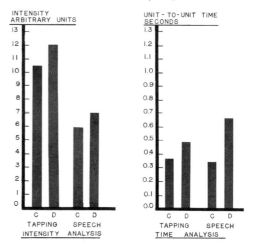

Figure 3-18. Differences in intensity and duration of tapping and speech under synchronous and delayed auditory feedback conditions. (Based on Chase, Harvey, Standfast, Rapin, and Sutton.[10])

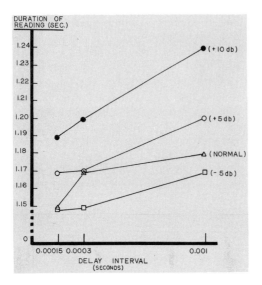

Figure 3-19. Reading duration as a function of accelerated feedback times, for different intensity levels. (Based on Peters.[49])

trends were consistent throughout the study.

The results of this study on accelerated feedback are consistent with the many observations on delayed auditory feedback, which have shown that retarded speech is associated with increased feedback time and increased intensity. Within a limited range, at least, speaking rate appears to be a direct function of the feedback interval.

THEORY OF DELAYED AUDITORY FEEDBACK

The discovery of delayed auditory feedback as a method of analysis of speech and hearing has led to the formulation of certain new ideas about the acoustic control of speech. As described earlier in this chapter, Lee[39] proposed one of the first theoretical accounts, in which he speculated that delayed hearing affects a specific level of speech control and thus leads to the various errors and discoordinations observed. Lee described the speech

mechanism as consisting of four types of neural loops of different levels and transmission lengths. The primary effect of delayed feedback was thought to be an interruption of the aural monitoring of the voice loop, leading to artificial stutter.

Servosystem Analogies

After Lee's original account, one of the main attempts to interpret delayed auditory feedback was made by Fairbanks,[18] who interpreted the speech systems in terms of a servomechanism analogy. A servosystem is a self-regulating system, e.g., a directional or guidance system which must be pointed by means of physical sensing devices such as radar or a human operator. As indicated by the diagram in Figure 3-20*A*, a servomotor activates the output motion of a device such as a pointer or gun, that must be directed and controlled in relation to a target or some other signal varying in position and rate of movement. The input of the system senses the difference between the output action of the mech-

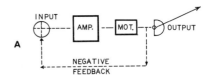

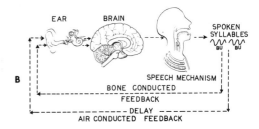

Figure 3-20. Servosystem analogy of the sensory feedback systems of speech. *A.* General diagram of a servosystem. *B.* Servosystem analogy of speech and hearing.

anism and the time, rate, or direction of the action of the target that is being followed. This differential signal (or perception of the operator) acts as a negative feedback, which in turn redirects the motor controls of the system in terms of the error difference. The sensing is thus accomplished by comparing the output of the system and the true rate or direction it should have. Inasmuch as the mechanism corrects its own errors continuously by detecting error between output position and rate and true position and rate, and then redirecting itself, the overall system is self-regulating relative to the action it is programed to achieve.

The general analogy of the aural vocal mechanism with a servosystem, such as proposed by Fairbanks, is diagramed in Figure 3-20B. Here the output mechanism is the speech musculature, arranged

to produce sounds according to a definite time and sound pattern. The sound pattern of this output is fed back to the ear in two ways—as bone-conducted and air-conducted sound—and is used by the aural system to control brain integration relative to the correctness of what has been said. This comparison in turn controls the succeeding words uttered. Delayed auditory feedback delays this comparative process, and, consequently, defects occur in the control of succeeding speech elements.

In deriving his servomechanism model for auditory control of speech, Fairbanks adapted to his purposes certain general ideas drawn from information theory and cybernetics. The general diagrammatic model proposed by Fairbanks, shown in Figure 3-21A, indicates little more than the obvious relationships in the auditory

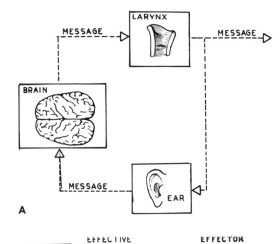

Figure 3-21. Fairbanks' analogy of the speech system. *A.* Elements of the speech control system. *B.* Model of a closed-cycle servosystem analogous to the speech system. (Based on Fairbanks.[18])

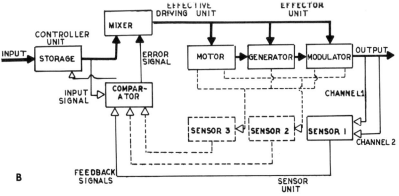

control of speech. Speaking involves the transmission of information, either as sound or as neural impulses, from the speaking mechanism to the ear, from the ear to the brain, and from the brain back to the speaking mechanism. The details of Fairbanks' analogy are shown in Figure 3-21B. First a distinction is made between the ear acting as a monitor in listening to speech of others and as an auditory feedback device for controlling one's own speech. In this latter function, the ear is a part of a closed-cycle servosystem that employs feedback to control the production of speech. This control system compares output with input and manipulates the production mechanism so that the output will have the same functional form as the input.

The analogy diagramed in Figure 3-21B equates certain components of the speech mechanism with parts of a servosystem. The components of the effector unit—the respiratory, vibratory, and resonant-articulation structures and mechanisms—are said to be equivalent to motor, generator, and modulator devices that regulate output. Receptor function is taken care of by the sensor system. Sensor 1 is the primary component for output take-off, the ear. The two separate channels represent the acoustic pathways to the ear through the air and through the body. Sensor 2 and 3 symbolize the tactile and proprioceptive end-organs. The sensor unit relays its data to the controller unit in the form of feedback signals. The controller—equivalent to the nervous system—is an automatic device that issues specific orders to the effector. It doesn't originate the message, but receives its instructions from a separate unit not shown. A stored unit of instruction, or input, corresponds to a unit of output and furnishes what is termed a control point. The purpose of the comparator and mixer are to modify the operation of the effector. They reduce the difference between the input signal and the feedback signal and the necessary

adjustments are then made to provide an effective driving signal to the effector unit.

The system has an important undiagramed characteristic. In the mixer, the rate of change of the effective driving signal is caused to vary with the magnitude of the error signal. When the error signal is large, as at the start of a unit, the corrective change is rapid. It becomes progressively slower as the error signal is reduced. An advantage of this feature is reduction of overshoot.

Chase[8] has proposed a rather general formulation of the servosystem feedback principle in order to account for delay phenomena. His view, which can be designated the recirculation theory, is

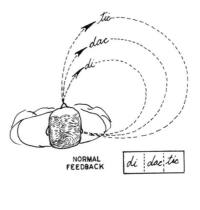

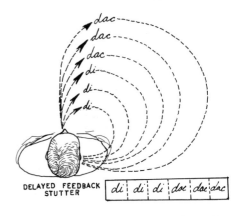

Figure 3-22. Diagram of Chase's[8] recirculation theory of the effects of delayed auditory feedback.

illustrated in Figure 3-22. According to Chase, normal utterance of a word involves successive discrete responses, such as speech units *a, b,* and *c,* each of which is controlled in order by the feedback from a preceding unit. The completed word thus combines the three units in proper number and order. The effect of delayed hearing, as shown in the drawing at the bottom of the figure, is to cause recirculation of each speech unit, thus disturbing both the number and order of such units in the spoken word. The word spoken with feedback delay thus contains an excess number of units in the wrong order.

Inadequacies of Mechanical Analogies

The phenomena of delayed hearing represent something new in the study of hearing and verbal behavior, not readily explained by traditional concepts of mental or perceptual control of behavior, or learning concepts. Recognizing the need for new theoretical ideas to describe the facts of delayed auditory feedback, Lee, Fairbanks, Chase, and others in the field have for the most part fallen back on analogies with mechanical-electrical devices. While these theoretical descriptions have the advantages of objectivity and the quantitative point of view, we believe that they are too simplified to describe the workings of either the auditory or the speech mechanism, and too general to provide a useful basis for prediction. Further, these analogies fail to take into account some established facts about speech, hearing, and behavior in general.

A primary defect in the servosystem analogies is that they don't account for the diverse experimental effects of delayed auditory feedback. As we have seen, the disturbance caused by delay is not a single linear function of the magnitude of the delay interval, as a simple error detection theory might predict. The disturbance varies greatly with different individuals, with the performance criterion used, with the type of performance required, and other factors. Further, some criteria show a peak disturbance with delay magnitudes of about 0.2 second—an effect that is not explained by the mechanical analogies.

Another defect of the servosystem theories is that they are not consistent with certain well-established information about the motion systems of speech. A number of detailed analyses, principally those of Stetson[70] and his co-workers, have given a clear conception of how the movements involved in speaking are specialized and organized to maintain the speech pattern. The central and critical fact about speaking is that movements of different types are involved in maintaining air pressure necessary for speaking, in pulsing the expelled air to form syllables, in grouping these syllables into various rhythmic units, in articulating in various ways to provide syllables with their vowel quality and starting and stopping consonants, and in adding tonal quality at the larynx. These movements of speech include postural reactions of the abdomen, diaphragm, and chest that form the breath groups of speech; more detailed movements of the abdomen and chest that give rhythm and accent to groups of syllables; movements of the chest wall that send air pulses through the vocal canal; and various smaller movements of the neck, larynx, jaw, mouth, tongue, and lips that articulate the syllables and provide tonal quality. The characteristics of speech depend on the organization and patterning of all these different types of movements. The neural mechanisms involved in the control of verbal behavior are undoubtedly differentiated at different levels to regulate and integrate the various movement components. The servosystem descriptions do not allow for the complexity of the neuromotor integrative systems involved in the control of speech.

Still another inadequacy of the theories proposed by Lee, Fairbanks, and Chase is that they emphasize the role of auditory feedback in speech production, while giving a less than satisfactory account of the role of kinesthetic and cutaneous feedback. Auditory feedback is normally a vital source of regulatory control signals for speech, but at times speaking can go on without audition or without sound. On the other hand, somesthetic feedback is undoubtedly essential for the intricate patterning of speech. The wide individual differences in response to delayed auditory feedback probably arise from differences in the ability of subjects to ignore the delayed auditory signals and depend on kinesthetic-cutaneous feedback. Such flexibility in control of speech is difficult to specify in mechanical analogies.

We must assume that much of the disturbance from delayed auditory feedback is due to interference between the auditory and other types of feedback. The fact that a peak disturbance has been recorded with delay intervals of about 0.2 second —an effect that remains unexplained in mechanical analogies—probably means that a maximal interference effect between auditory and other feedback occurs at about that interval.

Neurogeometric Theory of Hearing and Speech

As recognized by Lee, Fairbanks, and Chase, the study of delayed hearing represents a new level of analysis of the events of both hearing and speech. The main implication of this new operational approach is that the sensory control of speech is primarily an intrinsic neural process, the characteristics of which are determined by the basic sensori-neuro-motor mechanisms of perceptual-motor integration. A more general implication is that the perceptual and motor events of speech and hearing cannot be sepa-

rated, but are an integrated process in which sensory input is an immediate determinant of the properties and timing of motor response. These propositions are in keeping with the point of view that purely perceptual or psychophysical approaches to hearing and speech are inadequate to deal with the kinetics of these integrated events. We feel that a more adequate approach must incorporate our knowledge of movement differentiation, of sensory feedback functions in motion integration, and—in relation to auditory feedback—of the mode of action of the auditory system.

We base our own interpretation of the speech-hearing interaction on the assumptions of neurogeometric theory, as outlined in Chapter 1. Speech as organized motion can be described as made up of integrated patterns of postural, transport, and manipulative movements, differentially controlled by sensory feedback processes. Such control is defined by the detector function of internuncial neurons, which respond to differences in stimulation at two dendrite points. By this means, a movement—or its effect, such as a sound of speech—can be compared with some target or standard and can be corrected. Precision of motion organization thus depends on the sensitivity of sensory feedback mechanisms, including the auditory system, to spatial and temporal differences in stimulation.

Figure 3-23 diagrams the main components of the speech mechanism, and indicates how the different levels of movement are regulated differentially by sensory feedback—both auditory and somesthetic. We assume that there is specific auditory feedback for each level of this motion system that regulates the pattern and timing of breath groups, the length, rhythm, and accent of the foot in speech, the tonal base, and the great number of specific articulations of the syllable and their interrelations to form words and sentences. Further, we assume

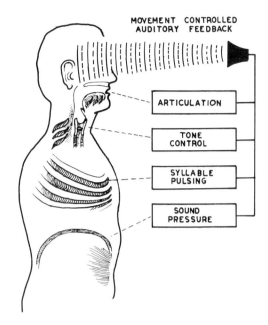

MOVEMENT CONTROLLED
AUDITORY FEEDBACK

ARTICULATION

TONE
CONTROL

SYLLABLE
PULSING

SOUND
PRESSURE

Figure 3-23. Differential sensory feedback control of the different movement components of speech.

that neural centers involved in the regulation of this system function neurogeometrically, i.e., the internuncial cells of the central system respond on the basis of stimulus differences and in so doing continually correct the motion pattern.

Our description of central neural action as being differential in function is particularly applicable to the auditory system, for some of the most clear-cut experimental evidence of central differential response has come from studies of the auditory system. It has been shown, for example, that single internuncial neurons in the cochlear nucleus respond differentially to specific bands of stimulus frequencies, responding to a wider band as stimulus intensity is increased. This neuron tuning has been demonstrated at very high frequencies as well as at moderate frequencies.[24] The best evidence indicates that basilar membrane response is very diffuse, especially at low frequencies, and there appears to be no basis for precise neuron tuning if

neurons respond as in-line conductors. A more reasonable interpretation is that the tuned neurons have ramified endings extending over a band of first order neurons, and respond when a difference in stimulation exists between two endings. This differential auditory response could be based either on spatial differences or frequency differences. Another demonstration of differential response in the central auditory system has been that internuncial cells in the medulla respond to minute phase or time differences between stimuli presented to the two ears, or to two points on one organ of Corti.[23] Also, the fact that nerve impulse synchronization with frequencies of auditory stimuli decreases as the central auditory pathway is ascended, until there is little or no synchronization at the level of the cortex, indicates that auditory discrimination is based on spatial differentiation within the higher centers. The central neurons are sensitive not to absolute frequencies, but to differences in frequency, phase, or intensity at two specific endings.

Neurogeometric theory of hearing and sound production assumes that such central neural detector neurons make possible the regulation of speech movements by sensory feedback processes. We assume different types of detector systems for the regulation of continuous or sustained and discrete component movements of speech or other sound production. Further, we assume that if an integrated speech or instrumental pattern is interrupted by delay of the critical feedback signals, the organization of the sustained and discrete postural, sound-generating, tone-generating, and articulatory movements will be changed. Thus, we believe that the variable quantitative effects produced by delays of different magnitude arise from changes in organization of the different movements. One such effect of delay is a degenerative change from the smoothly controlled phrasing of normal speech to the discrete, repetitive movements known as artificial stutter. This effect is analogous to the shift in organization of tracking motion from continuous pursuit to discrete movements when feedback signals are delayed. In both speech and tracking, the time characteristics and kinetics of the different types of component movements differ, and thus the various movements are affected quite differently by delayed feedback. The delayed speech studies indicate that the slower fricatives of speech (such as *f*, *s*, *sh*), which require sustained control, are more seriously affected by delay than the more discrete articulations.

SUMMARY

1. The most clear-cut examples of delayed sensory feedback are those involving a delay of stimuli produced directly by the individual's movements. Such delay was first produced experimentally in relation to auditory feedback, by tape recording speech sounds and then playing them back to the subject's ears after a fraction of a second.

2. In the original studies, Lee observed that delayed speech feedback slowed down speaking, increased intensity and pitch, and induced disturbances of speech, including artificial stutter.

3. With three subjects, Lee found a linear increase in reading time with increased delay magnitudes, but two subjects slowed down very little.

4. Lee described speech as involving a series of neural feedback loops for the production of phonemes, syllables, words, and thoughts. He thought that the voice loop was monitored by aural feedback and thus most affected by delay.

5. Quantitative analyses of reading rate and correct word rate have shown that maximal slowing down occurs with feedback delays of about 0.2 second.

6. Intensity of speech increases with increase in delay magnitude up to about 0.2 second and then tends to level off. Increase in pitch follows the same type of curve, not surprisingly, as the two effects are ordinarily related.

7. Speech errors with delayed feedback have been classified as substitutions, omissions, additions, and miscellaneous. All types occur most frequently with delays of about 0.2 second.

8. In an analysis of artificial stutter, Chase found that most subjects could repeat a syllable faster with delayed feedback than without. This might be due to a shift to a simpler speech pattern in the absence of immediate auditory feedback monitoring.

9. Delayed speech almost always produces emotional side-effects.

10. Children seven to nine years old were more disturbed by delayed speech than those four to six, probably because auditory control is less precise in younger children.

11. There is little evidence that subjects can adapt effectively to delayed speech feedback. One study showed some increase in reading rate with repeated exposures.

12. Aftereffects of delayed speech persist for at least two or three minutes after the delay is discontinued.

13. Disturbances comparable to the speech disturbances occur in nonvocal sound-producing activities with delayed auditory feedback.

14. Accelerating auditory feedback faster than normal airborne sound induces faster speech.

15. Several theoretical accounts of the speech mechanism and delayed auditory feedback have made use of servosystem analogies to indicate the intrinsic regulation of speech by feedback signals. In general, these accounts are oversimplified, do not explain the diverse experimental effects and individual differences, and do not recognize the multidimensional nature of speaking behavior.

16. Neurogeometric theory assumes that the different postural, transport, and manipulative movements of speech and other sound-producing behavior are regulated by sensory feedback mechanisms organized at different neural levels. Central neural action is assumed to be differential. Evidence drawn from auditory research indicates that internuncial neurons in the auditory system respond to differences in stimulation at two specific points.

CHAPTER 4

BLIND PERFORMANCE WITH DELAYED PICTORIAL FEEDBACK

For a clear-cut experiment on delayed visual feedback, the pictorial image of performance should be interrupted in its transmission to the subject's eyes. As we have said in the preceding chapter, the feedback delay in automated tracking is a secondary effect introduced by the machine system between an operator's movements and the movements of the cursor, wherein the delay is partial and variable according to the nature of the system. In contrast, delaying the pictorial image involves a complete interruption of the normal visual feedback of motion.

The only experiments so far reported on delayed pictorial feedback have been a number of television experiments that we and our collaborators have carried

out. Television methods have several advantages over the other methods that have been used to study delayed sensory feedback. By means of television and videotape recorders, we can record and feed back to the performer visual information about almost any kind of behavior. This flexibility has not been possible in other studies of delayed visual feedback. The television method of delaying visual feedback also has a marked advantage over studies of delayed auditory feedback, in providing complete control of the visual signal. In the auditory studies, only the airborne sound can be recorded and delayed. The immediate feedback of bone-conducted sound must be masked by raising the intensity of the recorded sound above the normal level.

Our television experiments on delayed pictorial feedback include studies of delayed feedback with "blind" performance and with concurrent performance. In the first situation, the subject performs a task without any view at all of his movements, while a televised image of his performance is being recorded. At the completion of the task, he is shown the delayed pictorial feedback. This type of study of *consecutive delayed feedback* requires only one videotape recorder, which is used first to record and then to play back the televised image. Preliminary studies of *concurrent delayed feedback* have also been completed, in which the recorded image is played back to the subject after a brief interval, while he is still performing the task. This procedure is equivalent to the studies of delayed auditory feedback reviewed in the preceding chapter. In this chapter, we shall describe three experiments involving blind performance with delayed televised feedback.

PROCEDURES

Our first observations on performance with delayed televised feedback were carried out with an Ampex videotape recorder, made available by the University of Wisconsin WHA-TV Television Laboratory. This recorder was used in conjunction with a closed-circuit television chain and motion analysis equipment in the manner shown by the diagram in Figure 4-1.

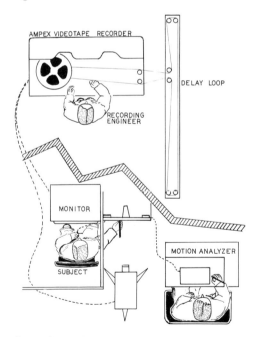

Figure 4-1. Diagram of Ampex videotape recorder and tape loop system used to delay visual feedback of performance. The motion analyzer times the movement components separately.

As in all of our studies of displaced vision, the subject was seated before a television monitor in which he watched the televised image of his performance. While performing a specified manual task, he could not see his movements directly because of a screen between his hand and eyes. In these experiments on blind performance with delayed feedback, the television monitor was blank throughout the task performance, and the recorded televised image was played back to the subject only after he had completed the task. That is, he saw nothing of his own manual movements until he had completed them.

The Ampex tape recorder was located in a different room from the camera and monitor, with communication between the two rooms achieved by an intercommunication system. The recorder was put in the circuit between the camera and monitor, and a tape loop was constructed to delay the visual signal by a controlled interval. The Ampex recorder uses a two-inch magnetic tape, on which the visual signal is recorded by means of a revolving head that scans the tape crosswise. The tape moves through the recording head at a speed of 15 inches per second. We adjusted the length of the tape loop so that it ran its course in approximately the time taken to perform the experimental task; for example, a loop 35 feet long would allow for a maximal task time of about 28 seconds. When the performance had been recorded, the recording engineer threw a switch to change from recording to playback, so that the delayed image then appeared on the subject's monitor screen. A photograph of the experimental setup is shown in Figure 4-2.

In two of the experiments to be reported here, electronic motion analyzers were used to record durations of movement components.[64] In using these analyzers, the subject is made a part of an electrical circuit, which carries a subthreshold current, by having him hold

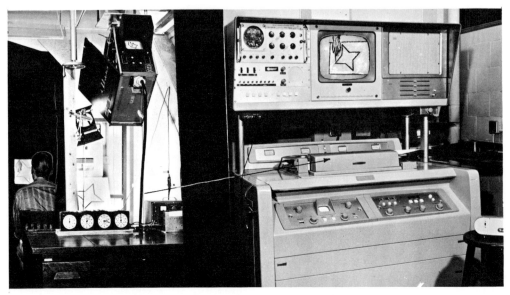

Figure 4-2. Photograph of the delayed vision setup.

an electrode in one hand and carry out his manual task with electrically conductive instruments on a conductive surface. The simplest analyzers are designed to time manipulative and travel movements separately. When the subject makes contact and completes the circuit, a precision time clock is activated and times the contact movements. When the subject breaks contact in a travel movement, the first clock stops and a second clock is activated. Thus, contact times and travel times are summated separatedly on the two clocks. The photograph in Figure 4-2 shows, in the left foreground, the four clocks of a four-channel analyzer, which is used in this case to time movements in four directions.

MAZE TRACING

In the first experiment carried out on blind performance with delayed feedback, the subjects were required to trace a mimeographed maze path with a pencil.* The pattern of the maze, which was 0.25 inch wide and 7.75 inches long, is shown by the stippled paths in Figure 4-3. Three preliminary practice trials were given, in which the subject traced the path with direct visual control of his hand. The instructions were to trace the maze accurately as fast as possible, and to remember the pattern in preparation for blind performance. Following the practice trials, the subject's hand was screened, his pencil was positioned on the starting circle by the experimenter, and he was told to trace the path at the same speed as before. Ten experimental trials were given, during each of which the subject could see nothing of his performance. Each experimental performance was televised and recorded, and then appeared on the subject's television monitor at the completion of the trial.

Results

Some of the results from the three subjects used in this experiment are shown

* This experiment was conducted in collaboration with Sherman Ansell.

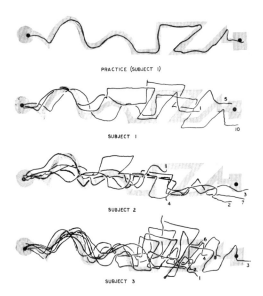

PRACTICE (SUBJECT 1)

SUBJECT 1

SUBJECT 2

SUBJECT 3

Figure 4-3. Effects of delayed visual feedback on repeated attempts at blind maze tracing.

STAR TRACING

In the second experiment on delayed feedback with blind performance, subjects were required to trace the four-pointed grooved star that can be seen in Figure 4-2.** The length of each leg of the star was 5 inches. In order to prevent the subject from using the sides of the grooves as continuous guides, small notches were cut along both sides of the pathway at half-inch intervals. If a subject attempted to slide his stylus along the edge of the channel, he was trapped in the notches, thereby increasing his tracing time. Thus, although he could not use cutaneous-kinesthetic feedback for a fast performance, such feedback did provide a check on accuracy. This situation is different from that described for the first experiment, in which the subject had no immediate check on the accuracy of his maze tracing.

The six experimental subjects used were given a preliminary practice trial with immediate feedback in which they were told to trace the star as fast as possible and remember the pathway in preparation for blind performance. For each experimental trial, the subject's hand was positioned at the starting point, and he was told to trace at the same speed as before. He could not see his performance until after a delay period of 25 seconds, when the recorded image appeared on the monitor. If he had not completed the star in that time, he was stopped before the feedback was presented by command of the experimenter. Ten trials per day were given in two daily periods. In addition to the experimental group, six subjects were run with immediate feedback as a control group.

in Figure 4-3. The tracing at the bottom of the figure is of one practice trial of Subject 1. The other tracings are selected test tracings, with those from each subject superimposed. The tracings reproduced are Trials 1, 5, and 10 of Subject 1; Trials 1, 2, 3, 4, and 7 of Subject 2; and the first six trials of Subject 3. Individual trials can be followed best by starting at the end, at the trial number, and tracing backward for some distance.

Over all, the results showed a poor degree of control in the blind performance, with some evidence of learning between the first and last trials. Subject 1 showed the learning effect most clearly. His tenth tracing was fairly accurate in size and pattern, although it was displaced to some extent. Subject 2 started poorly, foreshortening his tracings considerably. By the seventh trial, which is reproduced in Figure 4-3, he had improved considerably. Subject 3 showed little, if any, evidence of learning. As shown in the figure, the fifth and sixth trials were about as poor as the earlier ones.

The quantitative data from this experiment included the number of segments completed in a trial, and the durations of movement in each successive leg of the star. These movement times were

** This experiment was conducted in collaboration with Paul Greene.

recorded by means of a four-channel motion analyzer.

Results

The control subjects traced the star in a matter of a few seconds, without straying from the path. In contrast, the experimental subjects completed the task in the allotted 25 seconds in only a few instances. These blind performers often left the pathway and wandered aimlessly about, sometimes needing help to get their stylus back into the channel.

The total numbers of segments completed by the six experimental subjects in each trial for the two days are shown in Figure 4-4. The highest total for any one trial was 40, out of a possible maximum of 48. In Trial 15, for example, only two subjects completed all eight legs of the star, while one completed only six legs, one only five, and two completed only three. Although the subjects as a whole showed progressive improvement during Day 1, no further improvement appeared in these data during Day 2.

The mean times per segment for all subjects and all segments combined are plotted for the successive trials in Figure 4-5. Here again we see a progressive improvement during Day 1 in terms of speed of movement, but no further im-

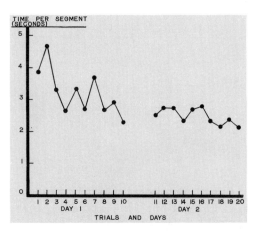

Figure 4-5. Effects of delayed visual feedback on performance time in blind star tracing in successive trials on two days.

provement during Day 2. The variation due to trials during Day 1 was statistically significant.

The curves in Figures 4-4 and 4-5 are roughly reciprocal but not exactly so because of irregularities in some of the data. For example, subjects would sometimes get out of the channel and break contact with the timing circuits, thus decreasing the recorded durations. In some cases, data were eliminated for subjects who did not proceed systematically from segment to segment.

DYNAMIC VERSUS STATIC DELAYED FEEDBACK

In a third experiment on delayed consecutive feedback, we analyzed the effects on performance of presenting dynamic and static feedback displays on the television monitor after the specified delay interval.*** The dynamic display was the sort of pictorial feedback of motion used in the experiments just described.

*** This experiment was conducted in collaboration with Sherman Ansell.

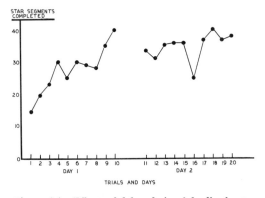

Figure 4-4. Effects of delayed visual feedback on total segments of a star traced blindly by six subjects in successive trials on two days.

The static display was simply a televised image of the results of the subject's performance—in this case the marks left by his pen in a dot location task. This latter type of feedback is comparable to what is called knowledge of results in learning research. Our primary concern in this experiment was to determine whether subjects can learn to perform a discrete localizing task blindly, with relatively long feedback delays, and whether such learning is more efficient with dynamic feedback of motion than with static feedback of results.

A second variable introduced into this experiment was space displacement of the visual feedback. We compared performance with dynamic and static delayed feedback in each of two conditions, with normal orientation of the feedback image, and with an inverted-reversed feedback image. This was our first attempt to combine temporal and spatial displacement in a controlled experiment and analyze their effects.

For the principal observations of this experiment, a constant feedback delay interval of 30 seconds was used. In an additional series of observations, using a normally oriented image and dynamic feedback of motion, the delay was set at 15 seconds.

The conditions imposed in this experiment are particularly applicable to the feedback delay problems that will be encountered in space science, if roving space vehicles are to be remotely controlled by transmitted visual signals. The relative efficiency of dynamic and static feedback, the effect of introducing spatial displacement when feedback is already delayed, the relative effect on adaptation of different delay intervals—all these are problems that must be considered in designing space vehicles and their control mechanisms.

We had certain expectations about the results of this experiment based on related studies of delayed and displaced feedback and on our theory of motion.

First, we anticipated only limited adaptation to the delay situation; we doubted that the subjects would learn to perform the localizing task with any great degree of accuracy or consistency. Second, we expected that performance would be better with dynamic feedback than with static feedback, better with normally oriented feedback than with spatially displaced feedback, and better with the 15-second delay interval than with the 30-second interval.

Procedures

The television instrumentation and procedures were similar to those used in the other two experiments just described, except that no tape loop was constructed to set the duration of the delay interval. For the dynamic feedback condition, the videotape was rewound rapidly at the end of the subject's performance, and played back to him after the specified delay interval. Rewinding could be carried out in approximately three seconds,

Figure 4-6. Photograph of setup used to compare dynamic and static delayed feedback.

and did not delay the feedback presentation. For the static feedback condition, the subject was shown a televised image of the task pattern after the delay, with the dots he had made in that trial. A photograph of the experimental setup, showing immediate feedback, appears in Figure 4-6. The monitor image shown here is oriented normally. For the condition of spatial displacement, a set of small switches located on the camera were used to invert and reverse the televised image. The television image was always slightly enlarged over normal size.

For each trial, a mimeographed pattern on electrically conductive paper was placed on the subject's performance board. As can be seen in Figure 4-7, the pattern consisted of an arrangement of 12 small circles, six in an inner ring and six in an outer ring. The task was to attempt to dot with a marking pen each of the small circles, zig-zagging from inner to outer positions in order, as indicated by the numbers in the pattern.

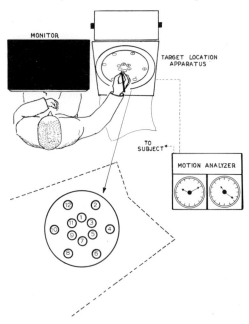

Figure 4-7. **Diagram of apparatus used for delaying feedback of dot location performance. The enlarged pattern shows the location task, with correct order of dotting indicated by number.**

The marking pen left heavy black dots that could be seen readily in the television monitor. Two types of measurement were recorded—the number of dots that were located within the small circles, and times of component movements. A two-channel motion analyzer was used to record separately contact and travel time throughout each trial.

For the main series of observations, 28 subjects were divided into four groups of seven each, with each group performing under a different experimental condition: dynamic delayed feedback with upright image, dynamic delayed feedback with displaced image, static delayed feedback with upright image, and static delayed feedback with displaced image. For these groups, the delay interval was kept constant at 30 seconds. On each of five days, each subject was given two practice trials followed by ten test trials. During the practice trials, immediate nondisplaced televised feedback of performance was given to all subjects. During the test trials, the monitor screen was blank during performance, and after 30 seconds the subject received the particular kind of feedback for his group. The groups that were to receive inverted-reversed feedback were so informed.

An additional group of six subjects was run through a similar five-day series of trials with a feedback delay interval of 15 seconds. This group was given dynamic feedback of motion, with a normal upright image.

Accuracy Data

The mean dot location accuracy scores for the first four experimental groups are plotted in Figure 4-8 in the form of learning curves over the five days of the experiment. Although the scores were low compared with the possible maximum of 12, it can be seen that there was a relatively slight but consistent increase in accuracy for all groups from the first to last day. This practice effect was sta-

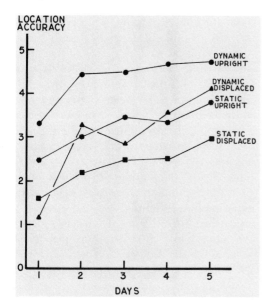

Figure 4-8. Mean dot location accuracy on successive days for groups performing with dynamic upright, dynamic displaced, static upright, and static displaced delayed feedback.

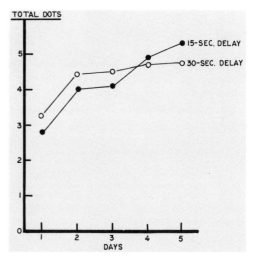

Figure 4-9. Mean dot location accuracy on successive days for groups performing with delay intervals of 15 and 30 seconds.

tistically significant. First-day scores were the poorest for all groups, and last-day scores were best. As predicted, dynamic feedback gave consistently better performance than static feedback, and upright vision gave better performance than inverted-reversed vision.

When the accuracy scores for all five days were combined to give a five-day accuracy mean for each group, the group performing with dynamic upright feedback had the highest mean, followed by static upright, dynamic displaced, and static displaced, in that order. The means for the dynamic upright and static displaced groups were significantly different from each other.

The graph in Figure 4-9 compares the accuracy scores for the group given dynamic upright feedback after a 30-second delay, and the comparable group given feedback after a 15-second delay. Over all, there was very little difference in accuracy of performance related to length of delay interval. It can be seen that the groups switched relative posi-

tions during the course of the experiment. Statistical analysis showed that differences in accuracy due to delay time were not significant.

Time Data

The recorded movement time data from this experiment showed more poorly defined trends than the accuracy scores. Mean contact times and travel times per trial for the five days of the experiment, for the first four experimental groups, are shown in Figures 4-10 and 4-11. All

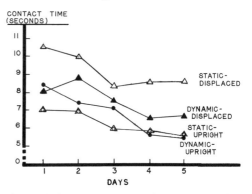

Figure 4-10. Mean contact time on successive days for groups performing with dynamic upright, dynamic displaced, static upright, and static displaced delayed feedback.

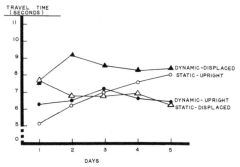

Figure 4-11. Mean travel time on successive days for groups performing with dynamic upright, dynamic displaced, static upright, and static displaced delayed feedback.

groups showed a slight decrease in contact time over the five days, but the differences between groups were not clearcut. The slowest contact times were given consistently by the group performing with static displaced feedback, but the other three groups were not clearly different from each other. The travel time means in Figure 4-11 showed no consistent trends from day to day, and no clear-cut differences among groups.

The curves in Figure 4-12 show contact and travel times combined into mean total time per trial for the five days. Over all, there appears to be a slight decrease in performance time from the first to last

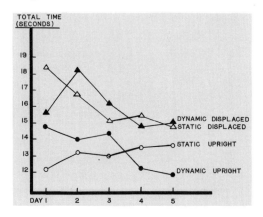

Figure 4-12. Mean total task time on successive days for groups performing with dynamic upright, dynamic displaced, static upright, and static displaced delayed feedback.

days, although the trend is not consistent for all groups. Performance with spatially displaced feedback was consistently slower than performance with upright feedback, but there were no consistent time differences between dynamic and static feedback.

Some of the ambiguities of these time data may be due to the fact that the learning effect was obscured by some other factor that influenced performance time throughout the course of each daily experimental session. The mean performance times for all four groups combined are plotted in Figure 4-13 for each trial separately on the five successive days. Although there is a slight progressive decrease in time from one day to the next, the trials on any given day (except for Day 2) show a general increase in time after the first trial. The daily pattern was to start relatively fast and then slow down somewhat. Whatever caused this trial-to-trial effect—emotional tension, change in motivation, or what not—it tended to obscure the day-to-day learning or adaptation effect, as judged by the movement-

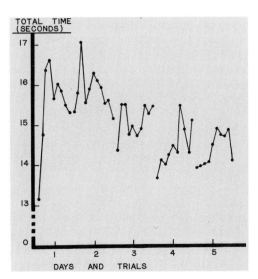

Figure 4-13. Mean total task time for four 30-second groups in successive trials on five experimental days.

time criterion. The accuracy scores did not show this same effect from early to late trials, but tended to improve somewhat throughout each daily session as well as from day to day.

The curves in Figure 4-14 compare performance after delay intervals of 30 and 15 seconds, for the groups performing with dynamic upright feedback. The group performing with the shorter feedback interval showed consistently faster total performance times. This total time difference was statistically significant for the five days combined, but not for the fifth day, whereas travel times differed significantly for all days and for the fifth day.

Conclusions

Our predictions about the outcome of this experiment for the most part were fulfilled. The most striking result was the limited degree of learning that took place with delayed feedback. None of the groups improved much in accuracy during the five days, and their speed of performance changed very little.

In general, performance was more accurate for the groups given delayed dynamic feedback of motion than for those

who were given delayed static feedback of the results of their performance. However, there were no differences in performance time related to these two types of feedback. When the feedback image was inverted and reversed, performance was both slower and more inaccurate than when the image was normally upright. This deleterious effect of inversion-reversal is consistent with our many observations on performance in spatially displaced visual fields.

There was very little difference in performance related to the length of the delay interval. Accuracy was approximately the same with delays of 15 and 30 seconds, although performance appeared to be somewhat faster with the shorter delay.

IMPLICATIONS FOR LEARNING THEORY

These experiments on blind performance with delayed feedback show beyond doubt that manual skills that must conform to visual patterns cannot be learned with any great degree of precision when the visual feedback is delayed to the end of the task. It is not enough that the individual see what he has done after he has finished it; he must see what he is doing while he is doing it. Motion patterns that can be performed readily in a highly precise manner with immediate feedback are disorganized and inaccurate when feedback is delayed, even after many practice trials. Because the visual feedback was delayed in these experiments until the subjects had stopped performing, the poor degree of adaptation cannot be attributed to interference and blocking effects that are so striking when the delayed feedback is presented concurrently with performance.

We believe that these results are significant with respect to the question of

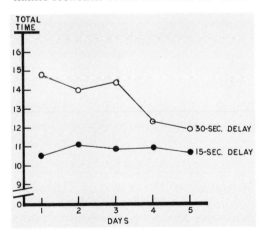

Figure 4-14. Mean total task time on successive days for groups performing with delay intervals of 15 and 30 seconds.

knowledge of results in learning theory. It has been accepted for many years that knowledge of results promotes efficient learning. While it is recognized that such knowledge is most effective if it follows closely the performance to be learned, it is generally assumed that even delayed information is beneficial. Thus, in some practical learning and training situations, knowledge of results is presented after considerable delay. For example, in recent years videotape recorders have been coming into use to make visual records of such performances as landing aircraft and other types of machine guidance, and athletic skills such as boxing, football, and baseball. The recorded televised pictures of performance are presented to the performers after variable intervals in the belief that such knowledge of results, even though delayed, constitutes an effective form of reinforcement and thus promotes learning of the psychomotor skills. The results presented here cast doubt on the value of these procedures. The positive effect of the delayed feedback must be small indeed compared with the effects of the immediate intrinsic feedback inherent in a normal performance situation. From a practical point of view, it would be better to improve the nature of the immediate visual feedback, i.e., to provide as many immediate cues as possible relative to the precision of the performance, than to provide any amount of feedback after a delay interval.

From a theoretical point of view, these results demand a re-evaluation of learning concepts, especially with respect to human perceptual-motor skills. The performance of skilled motions is defined by intrinsic feedback effects produced by the motions themselves, and only incidentally is affected by knowledge or feedback presented after a delay. Thus, the whole concept of reinforcement in skill learning demands reinterpretation to fit the facts of motion organization.

SUMMARY

1. Television experiments on delayed pictorial feedback have involved either blind performance with consecutive delayed feedback, or delayed feedback presented concurrently with performance. This chapter describes studies of blind performance with feedback presented at the end of the task.

2. The televised image of performance was recorded on videotape and played back to the subject's monitor at the end of the task. Electronic motion analyzers were used in some cases to record durations of component movements.

3. Subjects performed very poorly in tracing a mimeographed maze path when visual feedback was delayed until the end of the task. Very little learning occurred throughout ten trials.

4. In a star-tracing task, subjects traced around a four-pointed star with a stylus. The grooved pathway had notched edges to prevent tracing by feel. Subjects performing blind with feedback at the end of the task rarely finished the pattern in 25 seconds. There was some improvement during the ten trials of the first day, no further improvement on the second day.

5. In a third study of blind performance with delayed feedback, the task was to localize dots with a marking pen on 12 circular targets arranged in two concentric rings. Feedback was either dynamic feedback of movement or static feedback of performance results. Also, the feedback image was either normally upright or inverted-reversed. Delay intervals of 30 seconds and 15 seconds were compared.

6. Accuracy was generally poor with blind performance and improved very little over five days. Dynamic feedback was more effective than static in promoting learning, and an upright image more favorable than inverted-reversed. No differences in accuracy were related to the two lengths of delay intervals.

7. Contact times decreased slightly over

five days, but there were no consistent trends in travel times. Performance times tended to increase throughout daily periods, so that the day-to-day learning effect was obscured. Performance was faster with upright feedback than with inverted-reversed, and faster with the 15-second delay than with the 30-second delay. Dynamic and static feedback produced no time differences.

8. These results cast doubt on the accepted belief that delayed knowledge of results promotes learning. Far more important than delayed feedback are the immediate intrinsic feedback factors that normally define patterned motion.

CHAPTER 5

CONCURRENT DELAYED VISUAL FEEDBACK

The critical experiments on delayed visual feedback are those in which the feedback is presented concurrently with performance. The only experiment of this nature with true pictorial visual feedback, which has been reported by Smith, McCrary, and Smith,[65] was made possible by an unusual opportunity to work for a limited period of time in the RCA Research Laboratories in Princeton, New Jersey. Here we were able to use a dual videotape recording system, with heads for both recording and playback, by means of which we could present to the subject the delayed televised image of his movements while he continued to perform.

Further studies of concurrent delayed feedback in which the pictorial image was simulated have been carried out by

a technique in which the subject sees on his television monitor the hand of an observer duplicating the motion pattern of the subject. When the visible performance field is restricted and gloves are worn by both subject and observer, most subjects do not recognize the deception involved. The practical advantage of this technique is that it can be carried out with a dual closed-circuit television system and requires no videotape recorder. Another advantage is that the magnitude of the delay interval can be adjusted to correspond to components of the task, instead of being held to a rigidly controlled temporal interval. Comparisons can then be made between the effects of variable and fixed delay intervals.

Two additional studies of concurrent delayed feedback have been reported,[3, 31] in which the feedback image was not truly pictorial but was a graphic presentation of handwriting trace. We shall describe these experiments in the next section, and then proceed to the television experiments of concurrent delayed feedback.

DELAYED GRAPHIC FEEDBACK OF HANDWRITING

The first experimental delay of visual feedback was achieved by van Bergeijk

and David,[3] who used a telewriter to introduce a delay between handwriting
performance and the graphic feedback of
the script. A telewriter is an instrument
that transmits and reproduces on an electronic tube the pattern of handwriting
formed by a stylus point on a separate
writing surface. It does this by generating
voltages proportional to the X and Y co-
ordinates of the stylus movement. These
voltage values, $X(t)$ and $Y(t)$, were frequency modulated on two circuits and
passed through a delay mechanism, while
a third frequency-modulated circuit, $Z(t)$,
was used to record the time of contact
of the stylus with the writing surface.
After the delay interval, the signals were
demodulated and reproduced on the
viewing surface of a Memoscope. A diagram of this apparatus is shown in Figure 5-1. The subject was not permitted
to view his own hand directly, but saw
only the written words which appeared,
after the specified delay interval, on the
Memoscope.

A similar technique for delaying graphic
feedback was used by Kalmus, Fry and
Denes,[31] who extended their observations
to drawing and tracing performance as
well as writing. They used a telescriber,
which transmits electromechanically the
movements of a stylus to a writing pen.
Subjects wrote with the stylus on one surface, and watched the corresponding ink
trace produced by the pen on another.
They introduced a delay element between

stylus and pen that provided variable
feedback delays from a few milliseconds
to about a second and a half.

Van Bergeijk and David's Experiments

Two controlled experiments were carried out on delayed handwriting feedback, in both of which delay intervals of
0.0, 0.04, 0.08, 0.15, 0.27, and 0.52 second
were used. The test performance was to
write a pair of words out of a list of
twelve, with different words used for each
delay condition. The list was composed
of three 2-letter words (me, an, of), three
4-letter words (rose, dare, four), three 8-
letter words (graceful, hangover, pleas-
ure), and three 12-letter words (common-
places, overremember, prepossessed),
none of which contained an *i, t,* or *x,*
which would require dotting or crossing.
Six subjects were used in each experiment, and the order of presentation of the
words according to delay period was different for each subject. The principal
difference between the two experiments
was in the instructions given. The subjects in the first experiment were told to
write "the best you can." Time scores and
three-point neatness ratings (with 1 rep-
resenting the best rating) were obtained.
In the second experiment, using different
subjects, the instructions were: "You will
be scored for speed as well as for neatness
and errors; you should try to optimize
your score." Further measures of performance in addition to time and neatness scores were obtained by having an
observer report errors in writing to a recorder in terms of a code that indicated
omissions, duplications, and substitutions
of letters.

The quantitative results of these two
experiments differed somewhat, due to
the difference in instructions given the
subjects. In both cases, there was a marked
reduction in neatness as the magnitude
of delay was increased, and—interestingly
enough—the neatness ratings were very
much the same for the two groups of sub-

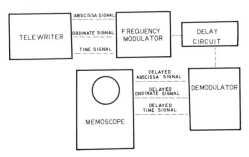

Figure 5-1. Van Bergeijk and David's technique
for delaying the graphic feedback of handwriting. (Based on van Bergeijk and David.[3])

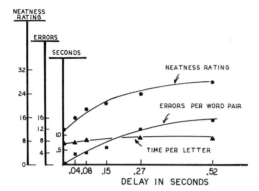

Figure 5-2. Changes in neatness, accuracy and speed of handwriting as a function of different magnitudes of feedback delay. (Based on van Bergeijk and David.[3])

jects at the different delay values. The time scores, however, were much higher in the first experiment than in the second, and there were *no* errors in the first experiment. The effect of the changed instructions in the second experiment, emphasizing speed as well as neatness and accuracy, was to minimize the slow-down and to introduce errors, leaving the neatness scores much the same. Out of a total of 41 errors recorded in this experiment, 24 were duplications, 10 were omissions, and 7 were substitutions.

The average neatness, error, and time-per-letter scores for the second experiment are plotted in Figure 5-2, as a function of delay periods. The neatness and error scores appear to follow an exponential curve, with no sign of having reached a maximum. The time-per-letter scores show but a slight increase with increase in the magnitude of delay, and it is not clear whether a maximum has been reached. These results can be contrasted with results on delayed auditory feedback, which have shown that there is maximum interference with speech at delays of about 0.2 second.[20]

In interpreting their results, van Bergeijk and David conclude that neatness, or the ability to form smooth letters, is independent of instructions, and declines with increased delay periods. Speed and

errors, however, are interdependent to some extent, and the writer achieves near-normal speed under conditions of delayed feedback only at the expense of accuracy in spelling words.

Kalmus, Fry, and Denes' Experiment

In this experiment, subjects wrote passages either from memory or from dictation. Delayed feedback generally induced disturbances of pattern, increased duration of writing, and errors in spelling and making letters. Errors of repetition, omission, and addition were noted. It was found that distortion and slowing down of handwriting increased with increases in delay interval over the range measured. Total time taken to write a sentence from memory (for one subject) increased linearly with delay magnitudes up to 0.5 second.

When subjects were asked to draw familiar symbols, such as a treble clef, delayed graphic feedback produced gross distortion of the patterns. There was a tendency to overshoot, that is, to continue strokes beyond their intended end point.

In order to produce measurable effects of feedback delay, these experimenters presented patterns (such as periodic curves) on the viewing screen and asked three subjects to trace them. These tracings were then used to measure accuracy, in terms of the area of error between the pattern and the tracing. Performance durations were also measured. Although both duration and error scores increased generally with increased magnitude of delay, the correlation between duration and delay was only 0.338, while the correlation between error and delay was 0.837. This finding contrasts with van Bergeijk and David's observation that subjects (in handwriting) could "trade" speed for errors. In these tracing tasks, the measured error appeared to be a direct function of delay interval in spite of variations in movement time.

Within their limited trials, Kalmus,

Fry, and Denes noted no improvements that could be attributed to learning. They did observe that subjects varied their mode of response in trying to adapt to the delay, sometimes improving performance and sometimes making it worse.

SIMULATED DELAYED TELEVISED FEEDBACK

Because a dual videotape recording system was not available to us in our own television laboratory, we devised a simulation technique for studying some of the problems and effects of concurrent delayed pictorial feedback.* The subject sat before a television monitor performing a manual task, and, after a delay period, saw a reproduction of his movements on his television screen. Although he was led to believe that the image was of his own hand, it actually was the hand of a trained observer in another room, duplicating the subject's performance.

The experimental set-up is shown in Figure 5-3. Two closed-circuit television chains were utilized to carry out the simulated delayed feedback. The subject traced with a pencil the pathway of a maze located on an easel behind a cloth that screened his hand from his direct view. A first television camera reproduced the image of his performance on a monitor in the next room, where it could be watched by the observer. After a specified interval, the observer duplicated the subject's movements on an identical maze on his own easel, where they were televised by a second camera for reproduction on the subject's monitor. Both subject and observer wore black arm covers and white cotton gloves; the subject was told that the reason for the black and white was to make the televised image of performance clearer. Great care was taken to avoid any movements in the image

*This experiment was conducted in collaboration with Sherman Ansell.

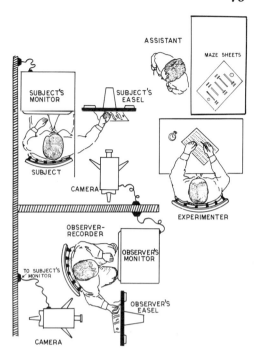

Figure 5-3. Dual interlocked closed-circuit television chain used to simulate televised feedback of maze tracing.

seen by the subject that could not have been his own. Between trials, when the maze patterns were changed, the camera trained on the observer's maze was masked, and a televised image appeared on the subject's monitor only after his hand was in place for a new trial.

The deception practiced on the subjects was almost entirely successful, for only one of twelve uninformed subjects expressed the opinion that the arm and hand he could see were not his own. The trained observer tried to duplicate each subject's movements as exactly as possible, observing the movement idiosyncrasies of each. In all cases, he could see the televised image of the subject's pencil tracing, so that when the subject traced outside the maze path, the observer reproduced the error. Later, when the error scores of the subject's tracings were compared with the scores from the corresponding tracings made by the observer, only four out of 55 groups of five trac-

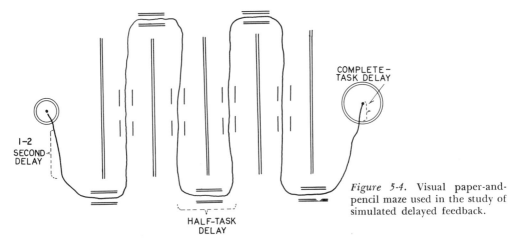

COMPLETE—
TASK DELAY

1–2
SECOND
DELAY

HALF-TASK
DELAY

Figure 5-4. Visual paper-and-pencil maze used in the study of simulated delayed feedback.

ings (a day's experimental period) showed significant differences.

Experimental Procedures

The maze pattern used in the experi-

ment, with overall dimensions of $8\frac{3}{8}$ by $4\frac{3}{8}$ inches, is shown in Figure 5-4, along with a pencil tracing made with simultaneous television viewing. The subject was instructed to follow the larger vertical alleyways, and also to stay within

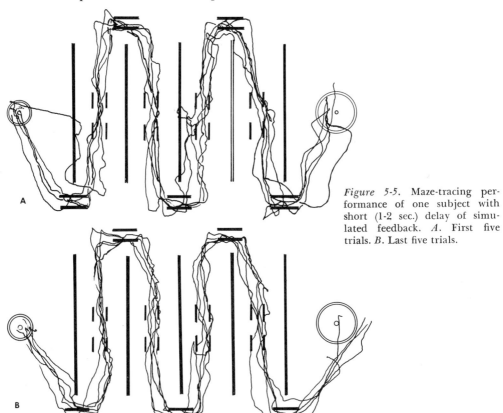

A

B

Figure 5-5. Maze-tracing performance of one subject with short (1-2 sec.) delay of simulated feedback. *A.* First five trials. *B.* Last five trials.

the narrower horizontal and vertical alleys placed intermittently along the path. The delay intervals used by the observer were specified according to components of the maze-tracing task. Three different delays were used: a short delay, in which the observer's hand started to move as soon as he could react accurately to the subject's movements (1-2 sec.); a half-task delay, in which the observer's hand started the task when the subject was halfway through it; and a complete-task delay, in which the observer waited for the subject to finish the maze before duplicating his movements. These three different delay intervals are indicated on the maze pattern in Figure 5-4; the observer started his "feedback" performance when the subject had reached the positions indicated. The positions varied somewhat for the short and half-task delays, within the limits indicated on the maze.

In the main part of the experiment,

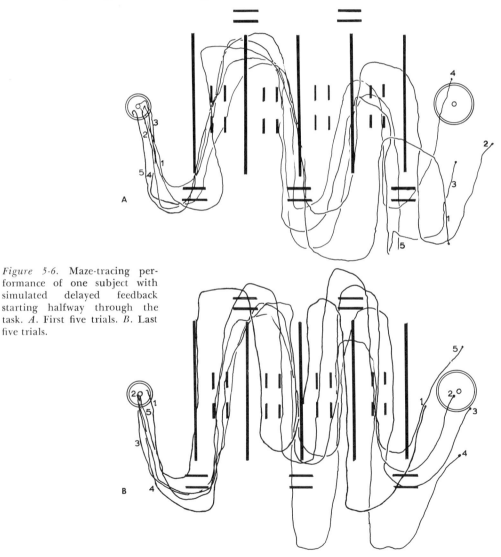

Figure 5-6. Maze-tracing performance of one subject with simulated delayed feedback starting halfway through the task. *A.* First five trials. *B.* Last five trials.

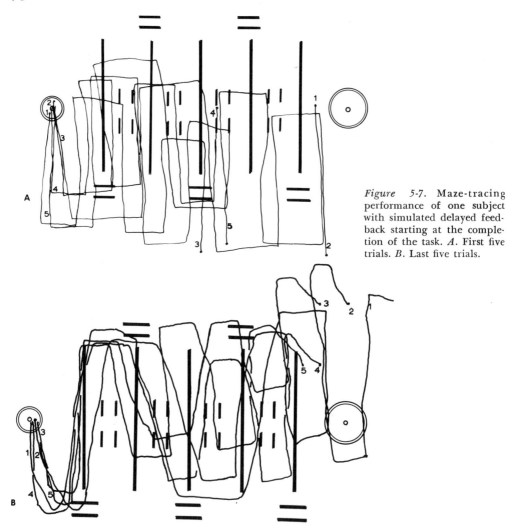

Figure 5-7. Maze-tracing performance of one subject with simulated delayed feedback starting at the completion of the task. *A*. First five trials. *B*. Last five trials.

twelve subjects were used, with four performing under each delay condition. There were three experimental periods for each subject, spaced two days apart, with five tracings completed in each period. For each trial, the subject's hand was positioned in the starting circle, after which he proceeded on his own. An image of the maze was visible on his monitor screen throughout each trial, and after the specified delay period a hand appeared on the monitor to duplicate his performance. The subjects were told that we had a means of delaying the televised image, and only one of the twelve indicated that he thought the hand he saw was not his own.

Qualitative Results

In general, performance was very poor in this experimental situation, under all delay conditions. In addition to the disturbances in motion organization, some of the subjects were emotionally disturbed by their poor showing in the task.

The tracings in Figures 5-5, 5-6, and 5-7 compare first and last day's performance of a subject at each of the delay periods. The five tracings from one experimental period have been superimposed. In terms of relative accuracy, it can be seen that the short delay resulted in the best performance (Fig. 5-5), and the complete-task delay, in the poorest (Fig. 5-7). Performance with complete-task delay is very like the blind performance studied with the Ampex videotape recorder and tape loop, described in Chapter 4. The principal difference between the two situations was that the subjects in the true

delayed feedback experiment saw nothing at all in their monitor screens during performance, while the subjects in this simulated feedback experiment were able to watch an image of the maze throughout each trial. In both experiments, performance with complete task delay was markedly inaccurate.

There were marked differences in movement organization between different delay intervals which show up in the tracings.

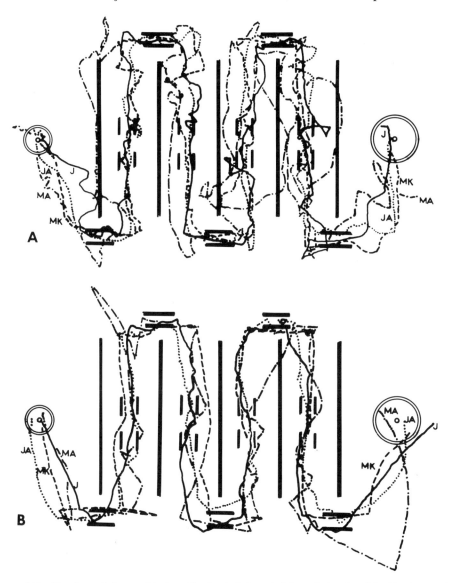

Figure 5-8. Tracings of four subjects with short (1-2 sec.) delay of simulated feedback. *A*. First trial. *B*. Fifteenth trial.

The tracings in Figure 5-5 show a jerky movement pattern that was characteristic of all subjects performing with the short-delay feedback. This jumpy progression through the maze usually began in the first trial, and was used throughout. With the short delay interval, the subjects tended to make a rapid movement and then wait for the televised image to "catch up" before moving ahead. Neither the records nor direct observations provided any evidence that the longer delays

produced these jerky, discrete movements. However, with half-task delay, as shown in Figure 5-6, motion was more irregular during the second half of the tracing, while the delayed feedback image was visible, than during the first half.

The different subjects used in each delay group performed generally in a similar fashion. Figures 5-8 and 5-9 show the tracings from the first and fifteenth trials for the four short-delay subjects and the four who performed with half-

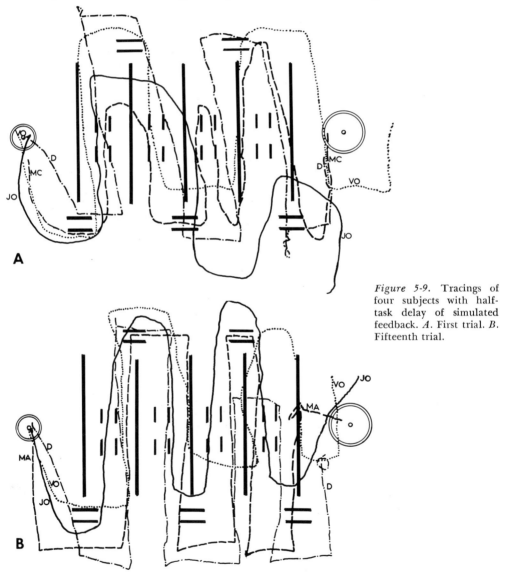

Figure 5-9. Tracings of four subjects with half-task delay of simulated feedback. *A.* First trial. *B.* Fifteenth trial.

task delay. The jerky movements are apparent for all subjects in the short-delay group, both in the first and in the last trials. With the half-task delay, there is no evidence of these jumpy movements, but performance during the second half of the tracings is somewhat more irregular than during the first half.

Quantitative Results

The maze path used in this experiment was designed to provide two measures of accuracy: a measure of "precision tracing" and a measure of "area tracing." Figure 5-10 illustrates how the maze pattern was marked off for scoring. One point was given for each block entered by a tracing. The large blocks gave the area-tracing score, with a maximum of 23, while the small blocks in the small alleys gave the precision-tracing score, with a maximum value of 40.

As we have indicated earlier, we compared accuracy scores to determine the degree to which the observer accurately reproduced the subject's maze path. Comparisons were made between subject and observer scores for 55 experimental periods, each consisting of five tracings. Nineteen of these periods were preliminary

practice runs to train the observer and test his accuracy. Only four of the 55 groups of precision scores showed significant differences between subjects and observer at the 5 per cent level, and only two, at the 1 per cent level.

The accuracy scores for each experimental group are plotted as a function of practice periods in Figure 5-11, and as a function of length of feedback delay in Figure 5-12. Both precision-tracing and area-tracing scores are shown. Each point in the graphs represents the mean of four subjects' median scores on a particular day. The curves in Figure 5-11 show a slight increase in accuracy in both types of score throughout the training period, indicating that some learning may have taken place. The most marked improvement occurred in precision tracing with the group performing with a short-delay feedback. The curves in Figure 5-12 show that accuracy varied systematically as a function of the magnitude of delay interval. In all cases, accuracy dropped with an increase in magnitude of delay. This relationship for the area tracing scores is approximately linear. It should be remembered that the delay periods in this experiment were not rigidly fixed temporal intervals, but cor-

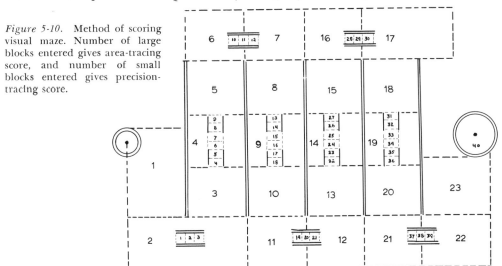

Figure 5-10. Method of scoring visual maze. Number of large blocks entered gives area-tracing score, and number of small blocks entered gives precision-tracing score.

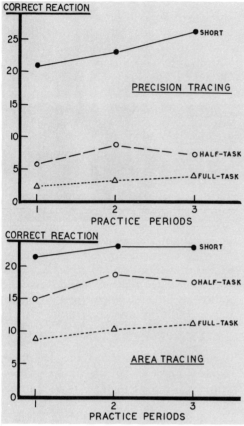

Figure 5-11. Precision-tracing and area-tracing scores as a function of practice for groups performing with different magnitudes of delayed feedback.

Conclusions

Although this experiment on simulated feedback sacrificed rigid control of delay intervals for flexible control in terms of task organization, there is no doubt that accuracy of performance decreased with increase in the magnitude of delay. Subjects performing with complete-task delay were least accurate in spite of the fact that their movements were not subject to blocking and interference effects caused by concurrent delayed feedback.

Movement organization was very different with the short interval of delayed feedback than with the longer intervals. All subjects performing with a feedback delay of 1-2 seconds progressed in a jerky

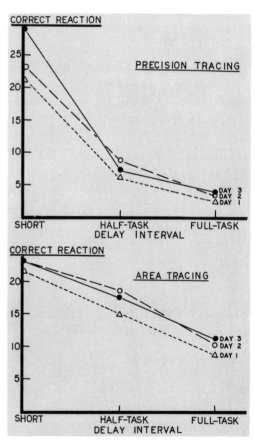

Figure 5-12. Precision-tracing and area-tracing scores as a function of delay magnitude on the different days of practice.

responded to components of the task. Thus, the means shown in Figure 5-12 are plotted at approximate values of 1, 30, and 60 seconds.

The differences between means have been subjected to analyses of variance and range tests to determine whether the variations in performance due to days of practice and to delay time are statistically significant. The results of the separate analyses of the precision-tracing and area-tracing data generally showed that the differences due to days of practice were not significant, whereas the differences due to delay magnitudes were statistically significant.

fashion by making a rapid movement, watching the delayed image "catch up," and then making another movement. Under conditions of half-task and complete-task delay, subjects progressed "blindly," but relatively steadily.

Perhaps the most important finding of this simulation experiment was that there was no significant improvement in performance over three days' practice periods for any of the delay conditions. The delayed visual feedback of performance did not effectively promote learning of the maze-tracing skill.

PERFORMANCE WITH CONCURRENT DELAYED PICTORIAL FEEDBACK

In order to study the effects of concurrent delayed visual feedback on manual performance, arrangements were made with the RCA Research Laboratories in Princeton, New Jersey, to conduct a limited series of experimental observations in their laboratories, using a closed-circuit television chain and two RCA Simplex magnetic tape recorders, one for recording and one for concurrent playback. With this critical instrumentation, we observed and recorded the effects of a televised feedback delay of 0.52 second on nine different manual tasks, involving writing, drawing, or tracing performance.[65]

Experimental Procedures

The portable electronic handwriting analyzer shown in Figure 5-13 was used to time separately the contact and travel movements of the different tasks. To use this analyzer, the subject holds an electrode in his left hand and writes with a metallic pencil on electrically conductive paper. A current of about 100 microamperes passes through his body when the pencil makes contact with the paper.

Figure 5-13. Portable electronic handwriting analyzer.

During this time a "contact" clock is activated, and when contact is broken, a "travel" clock runs. Thus, cumulative measures of contact and travel times are obtained. When the subject reaches the edge of the writing surface, he touches a small silver stop plate that automatically stops both clocks.

The arrangement of the equipment for this experiment is shown in Figure 5-14. The subject sat before a 21-inch monitor screen and carried out the writing, draw-

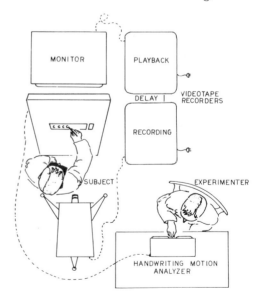

Figure 5-14. Arrangement of television, recording, and motion analysis instrumentation for the experiment on concurrent delayed visual feedback.

ing, and tracing tasks on the tilted table surface of the handwriting analyzer. He wore goggles designed to prevent him from seeing his own hand on the table below; he could watch his own performance only by viewing the monitor image. The camera was located so as to give an undistorted image of the performance area, magnified in size about 1.5 times. The subject could see in the monitor the writing area, his own hand and pencil, and his lower arm. To delay the visual feedback of performance, the televised image was recorded on magnetic tape by the first recorder and then transmitted to the monitor by means of the playback head of the second recorder. The tape distance between the two recorders (52 inches) determined the magnitude of feedback delay of 0.52 second.

The tasks used in this study are described in Figure 5-15. They were: (1) writing all letters of the alphabet, each one five times; (2) star tracing; (3) drawing geometric figures; (4) writing 4-letter nonsense syllables; (5) tracing a maze like that described in our simulated feedback experiment (see Fig. 5-4); (6) writing 4-letter words; (7) writing 12 words of different length (this was the list of 12 words on p. 71 used by van Bergeijk and David,[3] referred to in our chart as the "Bell Tel[ephone]" words); (8) writing 3-letter nonsense syllables; and (9) dotting six small circles of decreasing diameter ($7/8$ inch to $3/8$ inch). The number of trials and repetitions in each task are indicated in the chart.

The nine tasks were randomly arranged for the two subjects who performed in the experiment, both of whom were professional psychologists. They attempted to work as accurately and rapidly as possible. In addition to performing under conditions of delayed televised feedback, both subjects performed the same tasks under normal conditions, when they could observe their movements directly, and with nondelayed televised performance, when they watched

		TRIALS
STAR TRACING		4
DRAWING FORMS (3)	○ △ ◇	4
ALL LETTERS OF ALPHABET	c c c c c,	26 LETTERS
FOUR-LETTER NONSENSE SYLLABLES (10)	juvk	1
MAZE TRACING		3
FOUR-LETTER WORDS (10)	gate	1
THREE-LETTER NONSENSE SYLLABLES (10)	yob	1
"BELL-TEL WORDS (12)	of, four	1
DOTTING CIRCLES (6)	○ ⊙ ⊙ ◦ °	3

Figure 5-15. The tasks and number of trials used in the experiment on concurrent delayed televised feedback.

their movements in a television monitor. Unfortunately, it was not possible to record normal performance and nondelayed televised performance at the same time and place as the delayed televised performance, because of the limited time available in the RCA laboratories. However, we attach no great significance to the shift in locale, because of the familiar nature of the tasks.

Qualitative Results

The professional adults who acted as subjects in this experiment found that introduction of a 0.52 second delay between movement and visual feedback made their performance inordinately difficult and frustrating. The simplest of tasks, such as placing a dot in the center of a circle, was nearly impossible to

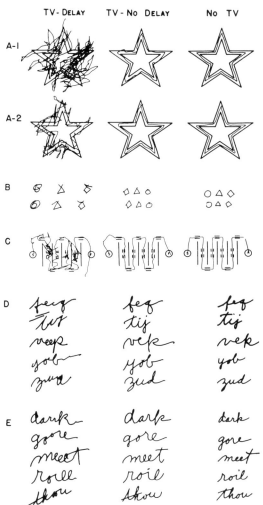

TV-DELAY TV-NO DELAY NO TV

A-1

A-2

B

C

D

E

Figure 5-16. Sample records of performance with a 0.5 second delay of visual feedback, with nondelayed television viewing and with direct vision.

were similarly affected. Handwriting of both novel and familiar material was severely degraded and, in some cases, completely illegible.

Some of the performance records obtained with delayed feedback are shown in Figure 5-16 along with records of nondelayed televised performance and normal performance. The star pattern with delayed feedback illustrates clearly the jerky, oscillatory type of movement just described. Oscillation is also seen in the maze-tracing task. The written verbal material, which showed the oscillatory type of movement to a more limited degree, was marked by a great decrease in legibility and the introduction of numerous errors.

An analysis of 64 errors in writing words with delayed feedback is shown in Figure 5-17. The greatest number (40.8 per cent) were letter duplications, examples of which can be seen in Figure 5-16. The predominance of this type of error parallels the findings of van Bergeijk and David. The second most numerous kind of error (26.6 per cent) was the insertion of letters or parts of letters. There were a few errors of omission (7.8 per cent) and a variety of miscellaneous errors in writing (23.4 per cent). The numerous insertions and duplications are

achieve with any reasonable degree of accuracy or movement control. Any kind of localizing movement, simple or complex, demanded extraordinary effort and had but poor success. Placing and tracing motions that are normally fast, uniform, smooth, and highly precise became erratic and jerky regardless of all attempts to control them. Tracing movements that demand continuous visual guidance became very noticeably oscillatory, and even the more discrete localizing movements

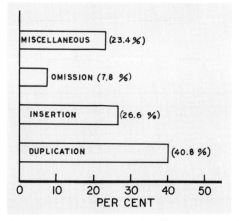

MISCELLANEOUS   (23.4 %)

OMISSION (7.8 %)

INSERTION   (26.6 %)

DUPLICATION   (40.8 %)

0   10   20   30   40   50
PER CENT

Figure 5-17. Percentage of different types of errors in handwriting with delayed visual feedback.

analogous to the repetitive articulatory errors induced by delayed auditory feedback, and might indeed be described as "graphic stuttering."

Evaluation of the accuracy of performance in the tracing and dotting tasks shows more dramatically than in the writing tasks the disturbing effects of delayed vision. Some of the records of star and maze tracing were so poor that they could not be scored. Performance in the circle dotting task was also very poor. About two-thirds of the time, dots were placed more than half the radius of the circle away from the center, and in a few cases, dots were entirely outside the circle.

Quantitative Results

The mean contact and travel times per trial for the different tasks under the three conditions are summarized in Table 5-1. The data for the two subjects are given separately. As indicated in Figure 5-15, the letter-writing task consisted of writing a letter five times for each trial; drawing of geometric figures involved drawing three simple figures for each

trial; and the circle-dotting task required dotting six circles. Time values for writing words represent mean time per word. The travel times given for the star-tracing task simply represent the time necessary to move from the star pattern to the stop plate. No travel times are given for maze tracing, as the measure was inappropriate for this task. Other missing data were due to equipment failures, etc.

The most consistent feature of the data in Table 5-1 is that performance time increased somewhat when the subject watched his movements on a television monitor instead of directly, and increased still more when the televised feedback was delayed. In order to see more clearly the relative increases in performance time, we have averaged the data for the two subjects and plotted in Figure 5-18 the relative times for each task under each of the three conditions, in each case letting normal time equal one. (When data were missing for one subject, the other subject's data were used alone.) Looking at the bar graphs for contact time, we see a distinct difference between the group of writing tasks and the trac-

Table 5-1. Performance Times with Delayed Televised Vision, Nondelayed Televised Vision, and Normal Vision

TASK	SUBJECT	MEAN CONTACT TIME (SEC.)			MEAN TRAVEL TIME (SEC.)		
		TV, DELAY	TV, NO DELAY	NORMAL	TV, DELAY	TV, NO DELAY	NORMAL
Letters of Alphabet	A	9.77	3.05	2.77	6.05	1.68	1.30
	B	6.25	3.55	2.62	2.49	1.61	1.41
Star Tracing	A	86.22	13.76	5.86	1.11	0.59	0.54
	B	49.63	16.02	6.28	0.50	0.52	0.54
Geometric Figures	A	6.10	3.47	3.49	2.38	1.31	1.22
	B	5.00	6.43	4.74	1.89	1.57	1.24
4-Letter Nonsense	A	4.08	1.99	1.64	——	0.62	0.54
	B	6.39	2.42	1.90	1.02	0.64	0.46
Maze Tracing	A	102.80	18.00	7.22	——	——	——
	B	107.57	23.92	7.55	——	——	——
4-Letter Words	A	4.30	1.69	1.49	1.48	0.68	0.50
	B	——	2.62	1.59	——	0.65	0.51
Bell-Tel. Words	A	5.88	2.50	2.24	0.74	0.58	0.41
	B	5.54	3.14	2.42	0.75	0.55	0.42
3-Letter Nonsense	A	5.08	1.72	1.42	1.05	0.75	0.52
	B	——	2.22	1.57	——	0.86	0.49
Dotting Circles	A	27.81	2.85	2.49	10.72	3.65	3.77
	B	12.68	4.05	1.69	15.37	5.44	2.27

ing and dotting tasks. In writing letters or words, delayed televised performance showed contact times from 2.5 to 3.6 times as long as normal contact times, whereas the tracing and drawing tasks were slowed down much more markedly, by ratios of 9.7 to 14.3. The one task with but a minor increase in contact time was drawing geometric figures. The effect of the delayed visual feedback can be assessed more directly by comparing contact times for the televised performances. In Figure 5-18 the increase ratios between nondelayed (TV) and delayed (DTV) televised performance are indicated to the right of the bars. Here again the ratio is insignificant for geometric figures, very much the same for all the writing tasks, and highest for tracing and dotting tasks. The tasks most disturbed by delayed feedback were those requiring continuous visual control. Less disturbed were the tasks of writing letters and words, and drawing simple geometric figures, in which there are established kinesthetic patterns of control.

The relative increases in travel time are in general less marked than for contact time, and show no clear-cut differ-ences for the different tasks. However, here again we see a consistent increase for televised over normal performance, and a more marked increase induced by delayed feedback.

In order to determine whether or not televised performance and delayed feedback altered the relative time spent in travel and manipulation for the various repetitive tasks, contact-time/total-time ratios were computed for each subject separately for the different conditions. No consistent trends could be found in these data. In some cases the ratio was significantly higher for delayed televised performance, but in other cases, it was higher for the normal condition. Interestingly enough, in some tasks the two subjects reacted in opposite ways, with one showing a significant increase in the contact-time/total-time ratio for delayed feedback performance, and the other showing a significant decrease.

Because only two subjects were used in this experiment, it is of value to compare their performance to established norms when possible. Normal data have been published by Smith and Bloom[58] for mean contact times for each letter of

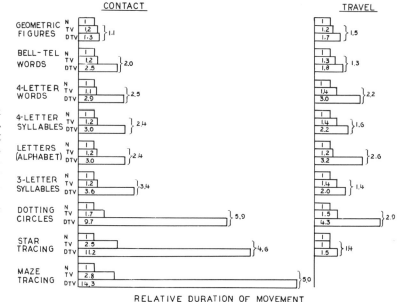

Figure 5-18. Relative contact and travel times of the writing, drawing, dotting, and tracing tasks with normal vision (N), nondelayed televised feedback (TV), and delayed televised feedback (DTV). The ratios between measures for delayed and nondelayed televised feedback are indicated at the ends of the bars.

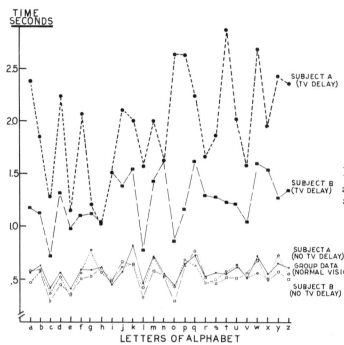

Figure 5-19. Contact times for writing different letters of the alphabet with delayed feedback and normal vision.

the alphabet and for mean contact and travel times for all letters of the alphabet combined. In Figure 5-19, these earlier means for each letter are plotted along with the data from each of the two subjects in this experiment under normal and delayed televised conditions. Here it can be seen that performance with delayed feedback in general exaggerates the variations found in normal handwriting. The letters that normally require long contact times were the ones written most slowly with delayed feedback. The variations in contact time among the different letters are particularly marked in the data from Subject A.

Figure 5-20 gives the mean contact and travel times per letter for all letters of the alphabet for the two subjects in this experiment. Mean times are given for normal viewing, television viewing with no delay, and delayed television viewing. Delayed visual feedback induced a threefold increase in both contact and travel times over normal performance times.

Conclusions

This first experiment on delayed pictorial feedback, concurrent with performance, provided a clear demonstration of the devastating effects of such delay. In spite of their foreknowledge of the nature and significance of the experiment, the subjects found it extremely difficult to perform under the imposed delay, and

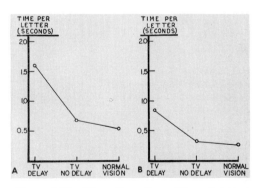

Figure 5-20. Mean times for writing all letters of the alphabet with normal vision, televised viewing, and delayed televised feedback of motion. *A.* Contact time. *B.* Travel time.

experienced emotional as well as motor disturbances.

The specific effects of delayed pictorial feedback were similar to those resulting from delayed graphic feedback of handwriting and delayed auditory feedback. There was a marked slowdown of movement; blocking and disorganization; repetition of movements; and changes in motion patterning. The incidence of errors in handwriting—repetitions, additions, and omissions—was comparable to the incidence of speech errors with delayed auditory feedback.

As might be expected, the motions most severely affected by visual delay were those requiring almost continuous visual guidance. Habitual skills, such as handwriting, can be monitored fairly successfully by kinesthetic cues, and were thus less degraded by delayed visual feedback than tasks such as maze tracing that depend on visual cues for their accuracy.

Because of the limited time available for this experiment, no observations could be made on possible adaptation to the delay condition. Other experiments on delayed sensory feedback have shown that repeated exposure to delay has produced little, if any, improvement in performance. Further research is needed to determine how well individuals can adapt to delayed feedback.

SUMMARY

1. For a critical analysis of the effects of delayed visual feedback, the feedback stimuli should be presented concurrently with performance.

2. Van Bergeijk and David delayed the feedback of handwriting script by using a telewriter and delaying the frequency modulated signals generated by the writing stylus. The script was viewed by subjects on a Memoscope after delays of 0.0, 0.04, 0.08, 0.15, 0.27, and 0.52 second.

3. Subjects who were told to write their best made no errors, but inverse neatness ratings and time scores increased with increasing delays. Subjects who were told they would be scored for speed, neatness, and errors slowed down far less than the other group, but made errors. Their neatness ratings were about the same.

4. Neatness ratings and error scores increased exponentially with increasing delay intervals, and had not reached a maximum. Time-per-letter scores increased slightly with increasing delay intervals.

5. Kalmus, Fry, and Denes used a telescriber to delay graphic feedback and found that duration of handwriting movements was approximately a linear function of delay magnitude up to 0.5 second. In tracing tasks, the magnitude of delay was more clearly correlated with error scores than with movement duration. Subjects varied their mode of response to the delay situation, but showed no learning effects.

6. Delayed pictorial feedback was simulated by having the subject observe on a television monitor the hand of a trained observer duplicating the subject's own movements in a maze-tracing task. A short delay of 1 to 2 seconds, a "half-task" delay, and a "complete-task" delay were used.

7. The subjects displayed emotional and performance disturbances with all delay intervals.

8. With the short delay, subjects used jerky, discrete, "wait-and-see" movements. With the longer delays, motion was generally smoother, although it was more irregular during the second half of the half-task delay, when subjects could see the delayed feedback.

9. Accuracy of performance decreased significantly as delay intervals increased.

10. There was a slight improvement in accuracy with practice (over three sessions). These differences were not statistically significant.

11. An experiment on delayed pictorial feedback (televised) was carried

out at RCA Research Laboratories by means of a dual videotape recording system. The televised image of performance was recorded with one recorder and played back concurrently to the subject's monitor with a second recorder, after a delay interval of 0.52 second. Nine writing, drawing, tracing, and dotting tasks were used.

12. The feedback delay caused severe disturbances in motion organization, as well as emotional reactions. Smooth, continuous motions degenerated into jerky, discrete, oscillatory movements.

13. Errors in writing words included repetitions ("graphic stuttering"), additions, and omissions and were comparable to errors reported in experiments on delayed graphic feedback and delayed auditory feedback.

14. Feedback delay caused a consistent increase in performance time of all tasks studied. Tasks demanding continuous visual monitoring were slowed down far more than writing tasks.

15. Further research is needed to determine whether individuals can adapt to delayed visual feedback.

CHAPTER 6

IMPLICATIONS OF THE DELAYED FEEDBACK EXPERIMENT

This summary of the known facts of delayed sensory feedback has been motivated by the conviction that these phenomena have far-reaching significance, both theoretical and applied. The experimental delay of feedback signals provides an entirely new approach to the analysis of perceptual-motor integration. We interrupt the intrinsic regulatory processes of patterned motion in order to gain new insights into the nature of the sensorineuromotor mechanisms that make such organized motion possible.

As we have seen, the number of controlled experiments on feedback delay is extremely limited, especially with respect to delayed visual feedback. Videotape re-

corders now provide the critical instrumentation for delaying visual feedback, subject to the technical difficulties and extremely high costs involved in using such equipment for sustained experimentation. Our hope is that these difficulties can be overcome.

In this final chapter we shall review some of the general facts of delayed feedback, as determined by the experimental studies and our own observations, and describe some of the problems that need further investigation. Special attention will be given to the problems of delayed feedback in the remote guidance of roving space vehicles, for, in space science, feedback delay is not a matter of laboratory manipulation but an unavoidable reality. Finally, we shall try to assess the theoretical significance of delayed sensory feedback.

GENERAL EFFECTS OF DELAYED SENSORY FEEDBACK

The different experiments on delayed sensory feedback have produced some inconsistencies, but, in general, have demonstrated remarkably similar effects. We shall summarize here the most significant findings.

Behavior Disturbances

No other experimental operation besides spatial displacement of vision creates such pervasive immediate disturbances in behavior as does delayed sensory feedback. Even a slight delay of a few hundredths of a second causes severe disruption or breakdown of normal movement integration, usually accompanied by some degree of emotional disturbance. Typically, there are reactions of surprise, startle, frustration, and loss of motivation to perform. These effects are all the more striking because the individual perceives nothing particularly wrong with the behavioral situation, except that the sensory effects on which he depends are in some way not aligned with his performance. Continued performance may bring about a deterioration in perceptual discrimination.

Delayed sensory feedback apparently affects all types of motions. Observations have been made on speech, singing, musical instrumentation, rhythmic clapping, tracking, handwriting, drawing, dotting, tracing, object manipulation, object assembly, panel control operations, and orientation. Some of the effects of delay are strikingly similar for different types of motion. These include blocking of activity; increases in movement time, intensity of action, and error; occurrence of incoherent activity; occurrence of repetitive movements such as stuttering in speech and repeated letters in handwriting; changes in movement organization; and slow and limited adaptation. The incidence of different types of errors—of omission, repetition, and addition—is much the same for delayed handwriting and delayed speech.

Most of these effects are most noticeable with concurrent delayed feedback, i.e., when the delayed feedback is presented during an on-going performance. Under conditions of consecutive delayed feedback, when a task is performed blindly and then followed by delayed

feedback of motion, interference effects and emotional reactions are much less marked. However, accuracy is greatly reduced in this situation just as with concurrent feedback.

Changes in Motion Organization

Continuously monitored movements are affected more severely and by smaller intervals of feedback delay than discrete "see-and-move" responses. It is in continuous movements, such as tracking or tracing a path, that we see most clearly the blocking, disorganization, and repetition effects. The individual may find himself unable to move from a particular point in space and may randomly initiate repetitious actions around this point.

Because of the near impossibility of performing continuously monitored motions with delayed feedback, they may degenerate into discrete movements. The individual performs a quick, discrete movement and then waits for the feedback to "catch up" before moving ahead. Although this sort of effect has been observed most clearly with delayed visual feedback, the stuttering effect in speech with delayed auditory feedback may be equivalent to the degrading of continuously controlled motion to interrupted discrete movements. The speech stutter can be interpreted as due not only to blocking of the discrete articulations of speech, but also to loss of control over the continuous movements of the chest, diaphragm, and abdomen that define the overall speech pattern and upon which the discrete articulations are superimposed.[70]

Quantitative Functions

There has been some effort to define quantitative functions relating degree of disturbance in motion with the magnitude of the delay interval. Some research workers concerned with tracking performance and speech have predicted that such functions would be linear, but they have been found to vary greatly with different conditions of delay and performance. Within experimental limits, performance efficiency generally decreases as the magnitude of delay is increased. As an exception to this general rule, studies of speech with delayed auditory feedback have shown a maximum disturbance in both speed and accuracy with a delay of about 0.2 second.

The difficulty in defining a quantitative function arises from the fact that there is no single factor that represents performance under all conditions. Motion patterns are multidimensional, and a single measure of accuracy or efficiency cannot describe a pattern under all conditions. The experiment on delayed televised pictorial feedback showed that the delay caused differential effects on contact and travel movements. Further, as we have seen, delayed feedback typically produces changes in movement organization, and may induce continual shifts in mode of sensory control of motion (e.g., from visual, to kinesthetic, to visual, and so forth). Thus the quantitative function of delayed feedback will vary according to the task and how it is organized with respect to sensory control and movement components.

Another important variable in defining the effects of delayed feedback is the individual, for there are marked individual differences in responding to delay conditions and in adapting to it. Some individuals are able to adjust more readily than others by shifting their motion organization to a pattern of discrete movements. Limited data on children of different ages indicate that the effects of delayed feedback are more severe in the 7 to 9 year age group than in the 3 to 6 year group.

Adaptation and Learning Functions

One of the most significant findings of the delayed feedback studies is that there is very little, if any, effective adaptation to the delay condition. Even after several practice sessions, any improvement shown by subjects is limited and quite variable. There may be more change within a single period of practice than over several consecutive days. The changes in performance that do occur with delayed feedback may be due not to learning but to shifts in mode of response— i.e., in motion organization—as, for example, when the individual substitutes discrete movements for continuously monitored movements.

The only performance involving delayed feedback in which moderately successful learning has been observed is tracking with velocity or aided systems. Individuals operating these tracking devices show definite improvement as a result of practice, although their performance never reaches the accuracy level of direct tracking. However, the delayed feedback in tracking involves only a partial delay, as contrasted to the complete delay that can be achieved with recording techniques. In tracking, the feedback delay is a secondary effect imposed by the machine system; the sight of the operator's own manual movements is not delayed. Further, in aided tracking there is immediate feedback of positioning movements, while the rate-control feedback is delayed. For these reasons, velocity and aided tracking do not provide a clear-cut example of delayed sensory feedback; while they show some of the deleterious effects of feedback delay, these effects are not as severe as with complete delay.

The poorly defined learning functions that are found with completely delayed feedback contrast sharply with the extensive and uniform learning that occurs in perceptual-motor skills under conditions of spatially displaced vision.[57, 62] The human individual shows great flexibility in adapting to many displacement conditions, including inversion, reversal, and combined inversion and reversal of the visual field. Further, normal performance is not noticeably disturbed by relatively minor angular displacements of the visual field, of the line of sight, or of the locus of vision. In contrast, individuals show almost no flexibility in adapting to conditions of delayed feedback. Highly organized motion patterns tolerate little change in their temporal regulation without breaking down into less highly organized and less precise movements.

When conditions of delayed sensory feedback are terminated, subjects show only momentary aftereffects, suggesting that any adjustments that have been made to the delay conditions are highly specific. Another indication of specificity is found in the transfer data from studies of direct, aided, and velocity tracking. Transfer from aided and velocity tracking, which involve feedback delay, to direct tracking, with no delay, was negative, while transfer between aided and velocity tracking was positive.

PROBLEMS FOR FUTURE RESEARCH

There are many problems of delayed sensory feedback that have only been touched on in research to date. In this section we shall indicate a number of problems of significance to behavior theory, although such a list obviously can be far from complete.

Blind versus Concurrent Delay

In Chapter 4, we have described experiments on what we have called "consecutive" delayed feedback, in which the subjects are required to perform a task blindly, and then are given the delayed visual feedback of their performance after the task is completed. This situation can be contrasted with conditions of concurrent delayed feedback, where

performance goes on during the presentation of the delayed feedback signals.

As we have indicated, the disturbing effects of feedback delay are most noticeable with the concurrent condition, when one type of sensory signal—visual or auditory—is delayed while cutaneous and kinesthetic signals from the same motion pattern are not. The interference between delayed and nondelayed feedback signals is probably accountable for much of the blocking and other disturbances that occur.

A detailed comparison of the effects of the concurrent and blind delay situations would make possible an appraisal of the relative effects of delayed sensory feedback and of interference between different sources of sensory feedback during motion. These comparisons could be made for both visual and auditory delay. One could also arrange a condition of intermittent delayed feedback, when the subject would be required to perform a task continuously, but would be given short playback periods of delayed feedback intermittently. In this case, there would be interference between the delayed feedback and the normal cutaneous-kinesthetic feedback only during the playback intervals.

Experiments of this kind would have applications in the human engineering field, especially in space science. If a feedback delay in the operation of a machine system is unavoidable, it is advantageous to know the most effective way to present the delayed signals.

Visual versus Auditory Delay

Experiments on delayed auditory and delayed visual feedback have disclosed many similar effects from the two types of delay, and also some differences. It is important to carry out more detailed comparisons between the two kinds of delayed feedback with respect to their immediate disturbing effects, the quantitative delay functions that might be derived, and the mode and relative degree of adaptation shown by subjects under the two experimental conditions. It would be especially significant to carry out such comparative analyses when the motion patterns are equivalent or similar for the two different types of feedback delay.

Another aspect of the visual-auditory comparison would be concerned with motions subject to both visual and auditory monitoring. An example would be a visually guided manual performance requiring spoken responses as well. It would be of interest to subject such coordinated visual and auditory feedback signals to both equivalent and differential delay factors.

As we have indicated earlier, we believe that some of the disturbances induced by delayed speech probably indicate the breakdown of continuously controlled motions into jerky, discrete movements, in much the same way that smooth tracking or tracing motions degenerate into a series of discrete movements. Further experimental analyses are needed to establish the validity of this interpretation.

Defining Quantitative Functions

An important objective of future systematic analyses of delayed sensory feedback will be to determine quantitative functions relating magnitude of delay with precision and efficiency of performance. Because no one function can describe the various and variable effects of feedback delay, separate analyses should be made of different motion patterns varying in complexity and organization, of different movement components, of different conditions of motor control, and with respect to other variables. Of special interest to human engineering research are possible differences between delay functions for unaided motion, instrument and machine control, direct and aided tracking, remote guidance of vehicles that move independently of the controller, and so forth.

Analyzing Perceptual Phenomena

There are many special perceptual phenomena of delayed vision and hearing yet to be described and analyzed. Delaying the sensory feedback of motion apparently alters all of the detection, discrimination, and qualitative functions related to the stimulus patterns that have been delayed. Accordingly, these different threshold functions should be analyzed under different conditions of delay and in relation to different types of motions and operational control of machine systems.

The procedure of feedback delay may prove to be useful in analyzing the coordination of receptor mechanisms in perception. For example, videotape methods of delaying the visual feedback of motion could be used to delay the visual image of one eye only, in an analysis of stereoscopic vision and coordinated eye movements. In this case, stereotelevision would be used in conjunction with a dual videotape system to delay the image presented to one eye.

Interaction of Delayed with Spatially Displaced Feedback

Analyzing the effects of delayed vision on performance carried out under different conditions of spatial displacement of the visual field is a possible approach to studying the interrelation of space and time factors in the regulation of animal motion. Our own theory of the function of the brain in perceptual-motor integration is that it is organized primarily on a spatial basis in responding to differential stimulus patterns, and that the sensory feedback mechanisms provide the basis for the temporal organization of patterned motion. According to this theory, the spatial and temporal patterning of motion are interdependent, so that delay functions describing performance relative to delay magnitude should vary in relation to the geometric characteristics of different types and components of motion. We can test specific hypotheses about the space-time relationships of different patterns of motion in terms of analyses of delayed and displaced vision.

Analyzing Specific Motion Patterns

In the past, our experimental studies of the specific neuromotor mechanisms of human behavior, such as handwriting, gait, artistic skills, object manipulation, machine operation, steering and tracking, have been limited to the traditional methods of learning measurement and correlational studies of performance factors. Procedures of delaying and displacing sensory feedback in relation to specialized skills and motion patterns provide us with an entirely new approach to the study of neuromotor integration.[62] There is no reason to believe that studies using these new procedures will negate the information we have already gained through general learning and performance study, but we are hopeful that analysis of temporally and spatially displaced feedback will add materially to our understanding of human skill patterns, including guidance and control of machine systems.

An outstanding characteristic of human perceptual-motor skills that has never been adequately accounted for is their specificity. Evidence for the highly specific nature of skilled motions is the limited correlation between them, and the small amount of transfer from one skill to a different pattern. We are hopeful that systematic analysis of the feedback relationships governing patterned motion may disclose the fundamental factors underlying specificity in perceptual-motor responses.

DELAYED GUIDANCE FEEDBACK FROM REMOTE COSMIC SYSTEMS

With the development of space science, the problem of delayed feedback of pictorial vision has taken on a novel significance. Any communication between earth and roving space devices involves an unavoidable delay occasioned by the time of transmission of electromagnetic energy through the distances of space. In any earth-controlled space vehicle, such as proposed lunar tanks which will rove the surface of the moon guided by earth-based operators, the transmission delay will cause the operator to receive delayed visual feedback of the results of his control motions. It is our opinion that the factor of delayed feedback will dictate the overall design and the operational control of these vehicles.

The problem of delayed guidance feedback in earth-controlled cosmic vehicles is illustrated in Figure 6-1. A television camera mounted in the vehicle would provide pictorial vision of the surface on which it had landed. The television signal would be transmitted back to the earth operator to provide information by means of which he could direct the movements of the vehicle. Control operations would involve transmitting signals back to the vehicle, and the return television signals would inform the operator as to the success of his movements. This whole situation is an example of unavoidable delayed sensory feedback of motion. The magnitude of the delay interval would depend upon the location of the space vehicle; round-trip transmission time between earth and moon would vary from 2.38 to 2.71 seconds, depending on the position of the moon in its orbit.

The only objective information available as to the effects of delayed feedback on organized motion comes from the limited number of studies we have summarized in this book. All signs indicate that a feedback delay of the order of

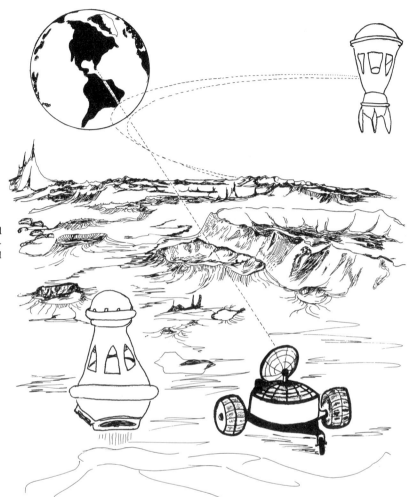

Figure 6-1. The delayed guidance feedback problem of earth-controlled cosmic devices.

magnitude involved in earth control of space craft would be seriously detrimental to guidance operations. The effects of delayed visual feedback vary with the type and complexity of the task, but all performances requiring visual control display gross disturbance with even short periods of delay, and accuracy tends to diminish as delay intervals increase. In addition, persons performing with delayed feedback typically show striking emotional disturbances and loss of motivation in task performance. Similar effects are found when visual feedback is displaced geometrically or distorted in certain other ways.

The experiment most nearly approximating the moon-delay problem was the study described in Chapter 5 on simulated delayed feedback, using a dual closed-circuit television chain. In this study, we explored the effects of variable delay intervals, from roughly a second to a minute in length; the subject was required to trace a pathway through channels and around obstacles; and we studied the effects of several days' practice with the delayed feedback. These conditions might all be involved in the space problem of delayed feedback. Further, we compared some of the effects of concurrent and consecutive delayed feedback—a comparison that must surely be made for cosmic devices. None of our results was hopeful for the guidance problems that will be encountered in earth-based control of space craft. For this reason, we have been interested in defining a program of research on the basic scientific and human engineering problems of delayed guidance feedback in space science.

To our knowledge, the role of delayed guidance feedback in the control of remote space craft has not been considered a significant factor in the preliminary stages of planning and design of these craft. Because the problems encountered here are new in behavior science, we believe that they will demand new conceptions of design, control, and training not heretofore encountered in either surface devices or aircraft. Before earth-controlled space vehicles are built and launched, it is imperative that the conditions of their control be simulated and subjected to experimental analysis.

The critical instrumentation for simulating the conditions of delayed guidance feedback of space vehicles is a dual video-tape system for simultaneous recording and playback of pictorial visual information. A complete systems simulation could be arranged by combining videotape recorders with a remotely controlled model vehicle equipped with a television eye. Such a system could be used to test preliminary designs and to test and train operators, in addition to its use in basic scientific research of the phenomena of delayed sensory feedback.

A similar simulation system could be set up for preliminary studies of the conditions of control of manned vehicles in space, in which control operations can be executed both from an earth station and from within the vehicle. In such a situation, there would be delayed visual feedback to the earth operator of the effects of his own actions, and there would also be both visual and auditory delay in the communication systems be-

tween the earth operator and the vehicle operator. To simulate these conditions, videotape instrumentation would be combined with audiotape systems to analyze problems of coordinating speech and sight control when both the auditory and visual signals are delayed.

Human factors analysis of the design and operation of remote cosmic systems is an area of behavior science that is as yet largely unexplored. The central factors to be investigated in this research area are those of delayed sensory feedback in guidance operations, with the special features of pictorial vision, substitute visual control rather than direct control, variable rather than fixed feedback delays, differential delay factors in both input and detection phases of the guidance system, and possible differential delays in communication and instrumental control. In addition to being delayed, the visual feedback signals will undoubtedly be intermittent, and subject to a certain amount of geometric displacement. We need to know what characteristics of control, perceptual display, and integration of control and display mechanisms a system must have in order to steer a moving device at certain speeds under certain conditions of delayed, displaced, and intermittent feedback. Only an extensive research program can deal effectively with these problems.

THEORETICAL INTERPRETATIONS

Although research on the effects of delayed feedback is relatively new and limited in scope, the results obtained begin to add up to a considerable body of evidence concerning the organization and control of behavior. The fact that all motions studied under conditions of delayed feedback were disturbed and changed by even small delay intervals indicates that we are dealing here with a basic mechanism of motion integration, of as general significance to behavior as, for example, learning.

Unfortunately, no attempts other than our own have been made to assess the general significance of feedback delay for behavior theory. However, there is a tendency among psychologists to account for the phenomena of sensory feedback, along with most other aspects of behavior organization, in terms of learning theory. The implications of this type of analysis are clear. If sensory feedback is interpreted as reinforcement, or as knowledge of results, then a feedback delay interval of the order of magnitude of those used in most experiments would have but a minor effect on learning. However, all studies of delayed feedback have shown that all delay intervals tested are seriously disturbing to behavior organization. We believe that sensory feedback processes are an aspect of neurophysiological control of behavior more fundamental than the temporal relationships involved in learning discrete reactions, that the feedback regulatory mechanisms are built-in components of the behaving system, as necessary to organized behavior as the receptors and effectors. Feedback delay interrupts the regulatory pattern and consequently disturbs the intrinsic organization of motion.

There have been limited theoretical accounts of sensory feedback and its delay in relation to tracking behavior and delayed feedback in speech. We shall review these concepts briefly in relation to our own theoretical position.

Visual Feedback Control of Tracking

As we have indicated in Chapter 2, there have been several theoretical descriptions of tracking behavior that attempt to reduce it to a single function. The movements of tracking have been described as discrete responses, all alike, separated in time by reaction-time or perception-time intervals.[46, 52] Another widely accepted view of tracking performance describes it in terms of learning concepts, with visual feedback from the target-cursor display serving to reinforce correct responses by providing knowledge of results.[5, 21] Tracking has also been explained in terms of machine analogies[52] and related mathematical functions.[36] None of these oversimplified views has been confirmed by controlled experimental analyses of the motion patterns involved in direct, aided, and velocity tracking.

One of the critical experimental findings about direct pursuit tracking is that it is defined only incidentally by learning, for individuals typically can track moving stimuli with a high degree of precision even before training. However, the artificial conditions of velocity, aided, and compensatory tracking disrupt normal patterns of integration, and the new patterns are subject to more marked learning effects. Another clear experimental finding is that tracking is made up of two main component movements: travel or rate-control movements, and manipulative or positioning movements. Introducing velocity or aided tracking control or a compensatory display changes the relative frequency of the different types of movements as well as their pattern of integration. Thus tracking performance is quite different with the different machine systems.

Our theoretical assumption has been that the continuous visual control of tracking that accounts for its precision is achieved by sensory feedback mechanisms that provide a continuous monitoring of the relative positions of target and cursor. Accuracy in such a regulatory system would depend on speed of transmission of the feedback signals from the visual display to the eye; any delay would tend to reduce the precision of the performance. Since both velocity and aided tracking systems introduce delays into the visual feedback to the tracker, we would expect them to be less effective means of control than direct pursuit tracking. Experimental studies of the effects of transmission lags and of the relative accuracy of different systems have confirmed our expectation that feedback delay is detrimental to tracking accuracy.

Neither the conventional learning accounts of tracking, servosystem analogies, mathematical analyses, nor the intermittency hypothesis can explain the critical data on tracking performance. They can't account for differences between the types of tracking or for the variable nature of the movement pattern in different types. They can't predict the superiority of one type of system over another, or one type of display over another. The precision of tracking is affected by many variables—target speed, complexity of target course, aiding and automation factors, type of display, and so forth—all of which can be assessed in terms of their effects on the space and time relationships in feedback control of multidimensional tracking movements. Consequently, we believe that the phenomena of tracking are best described by neurogeometric theory.

Auditory Feedback Control of Speech

Investigators who have studied the effects of delayed auditory feedback generally have assumed that speech consists of a series of discrete responses controlled by a feedback system that acts as an intermittent detector of speech sound units. The speech system, especially the part concerned with voice production, is likened to a discrete error-correction servosystem, which acts stepwise in directing its output. This conception, as stated by Lee,[39] and reiterated by Fairbanks[18] and Chase,[8] assigns to the speaker the simplest level of functional control of self-regulating machine systems, i.e., the level of control comparable to the linear amplifier. According to this view, the error in

speaking should be a linear function of the magnitude of delay interval.

The simple servosystem model of speech has not been upheld by experimental results of delayed feedback studies. The function relating error and delay interval has not been found to be linear; data on correct word rate indicated a maximal disturbance at 0.2 second. This peaking effect, along with the diversity of types of errors made with delayed feedback and the occurrence of blocking and stuttering, all testify to the multidimensional nature of speech and of its control systems. We believe that different types of movements are involved in speech—postural support movements, the continuous movements that sustain air pressure, and discrete articulatory movements[70]—and that they are controlled differentially by stimulus feedback mechanisms. Different magnitudes of delay would alter the control processes, and affect the interaction of movement components in different ways.

A meaningful account of the auditory feedback control of speech must consider the events of delayed auditory feedback as well as certain recent findings about the central neural system of hearing. There is experimental evidence to show that: (a) the cochlear nucleus contains internuncial neurons that respond differentially to specific sound frequencies;[24, 25] (b) some internuncial cells in the medulla are precisely tuned to minute differences in phase or time between the two ears, or between two points on one organ of Corti;[23] (c) the central pathway of hearing shows progressively poorer nerve impulse synchronization with respect to stimulus frequency from cochlear nucleus to cortex,[16] instead of the progressively better neural differentiation that would be predicted by traditional perception and learning doctrine.

We believe that all of these facts about the hearing system and delayed auditory feedback in speech production indicate that the fundamental mode of action of the nervous system in behavior integration is that of differential detection, by means of individual internuncial neurons that are sensitive to stimulus differences between two particular points. This concept of neuron action, which we have described in Chapter 1, contrasts sharply with the Sherringtonian concept of synaptic integration. We believe that it is the nerve cell itself and not the blank space between cells that determines the pattern of neuromotor response. A detector cell conducts only when a difference in stimulation exists between two dendrite points, reflecting a stimulus difference between two points on the sensory surfaces of the body. These two points might be in the same inner ear, or on corresponding points of the two ears. We assume that each such detector cell has a differential threshold that determines its sensitivity to spatial differences in stimuli, and a response latency that determines its sensitivity to temporal differences in stimuli. Thus both spatial and temporal organization of motion would be defined by neurogeometric detector systems. An on-going motion pattern such as speech would be continuously monitored by central detection of spatial and temporal differences in feedback signals.

Neurogeometric theory of hearing and sound production assumes different types of internuncial detector systems for the regulation of both continuous and discrete movements of sound production and speech. We assume further that the central system would be organized at different neural levels for the integration of postural, transport, and manipulative (e.g., articulative) components that are involved in all complex motions, including sound production and speech. If an integrated pattern is interrupted by delaying critical feedback signals, the organization of movements is disturbed and changed. Thus we believe that the variable effects related to different delay intervals and different types of response,

and the shifts in motion organization with delayed feedback are due to the multidimensional nature of the motion patterns. Normal motion patterns involve several kinds of feedback and several kinds of component motions; thus a disturbance in the normal integration will have variable results.

Precise feedback control is characteristic of sound-production and sound-controlled behavior in many animal forms. Stridulation in insects; mating calls, song making, and sound mimicking in birds; echo-ranging and orientation in bats, porpoises, and whales; complex vocalization in apes; and the extensive human sound production activities in speech, singing, instrumental music, and noise making—all these and other activities involve integration of continuous and discrete postural, transport, and manipulative movements to control the frequency, intensity, complexity, and time characteristics of sound feedback as both a result and source of stimulation. The concepts of neurogeometric theory account for the unified nature of the perceptual and motor events of the audio-motor system and explain the disturbing effects of delayed auditory feedback on sound production behavior.

Delayed Pictorial Visual Feedback

We consider the television studies of delayed pictorial vision the most clear-cut experimental situations yet devised for analyzing the effects of delayed sensory feedback. Television methods permit study of many different kinds of human activity, they provide precise control of the feedback signal, and they provide a means by which visual feedback of motion can be displaced both spatially and temporally. Using television techniques, we can study the organization of animal motion and its related perceptual processes in precise quantitative terms.

Our experiments on delayed pictorial feedback have been based on the concepts of neurogeometric theory and have been planned according to earlier experiments on spatially displaced feedback of motion. Our predictions of the effects of feedback delay have been that the effects would vary: (a) with the different component movements (travel and manipulative) involved in a motion; (b) with the complexity of a motion; (c) with the degree of continuous control involved in the motion; (d) with the degree of space displacement involved; (e) with the magnitude of the delay; and (f) with the type of delayed feedback, whether concurrent or consecutive. The limited studies we have been able to carry out to date generally confirm these predictions, and thus support the theory upon which they were based.

Learning Theory and Audiovisual Factors in Education

The analysis of delayed sensory feedback and related studies of space displaced vision have their broadest significance in defining a new context for research on human learning and educational design. As we have noted above, the major phenomena of delayed vision and hearing cast doubt on the central postulate of orthodox learning theory— that human behavior is organized primarily in terms of temporal association of separate stimulus and response units. All of the effects of delayed and displaced sensory feedback suggest that learning processes in man and animals are qualified by the spatial interrelationships between movements and their sensory feedback patterns. Thus the effectiveness of human learning situations and reinforcements must be understood in terms of spatial factors related to human behavioral design, which in turn define the intrinsic temporal relations in motion and feedback patterns.

To define an effective learning situation, we must understand first of all the space-time pattern of the motions to be learned. We have seen that the basic component movements in motion—the postural reactions that support the body in relation to gravity, the dynamic transport action of the body and its members, and the fine manipulative movements of terminal members—are all space-structured and controlled primarily by neurogeometric mechanisms relating specific movements and their sensory feedback effects. Learning is a process of establishing new spatial relationships in motion patterns. The flexibility of human behavior reflects the large number of specific spatial patterns that can be learned, and the observed specificity of human perceptual-motor responses derives from the spatial patterning of movements and their sensory feedback effects. In the human system, the number of specific behavior patterns of varying movement-feedback geometricity that can be performed is practically unlimited.

The course and rate of learning specific motions are determined to a significant extent by the geometric organization of those motions and by the spatial discrepancy between sensory and motor patterns. Inasmuch as the finer manipulative movements have the most complex and precise organization, they tend to be distorted more by delayed and displaced feedback than the more generalized transport and postural movements. However, the learning that does occur under conditions of displaced or delayed feedback affects the manipulative and terminal transport movements more than posture and large transport. This difference reflects a fundamental difference in movement organization; the finer movements are organized primarily according to the spatial requirements of the external environment, and must be adapted to many variations in stimulus patterns, whereas the more generalized transport and postural movements are to a large extent intrinsically organized, according to genetically determined mechanisms. Thus new spatially defined movement-feedback relationships of the finer motion patterns are learned in a context of intrinsically organized general motion patterns. From the beginning of life, the genetically determined movement systems of the body influence the pattern and organization of the more specific motions and their reorganization through learning.

The experimental results from studies of delayed vision and hearing show quite clearly that the time requirements of refined visually guided motions or of speech are relatively inflexible. New space relationships between movement and sensory feedback can be learned with little trouble, but the time relationships do not yield to learning or training. We accept this fact as favoring the assumption that the neural learning process in man involves primarily the establishment of new and different neurogeometric patterns of activity within the brain. The individual learns by acquiring new space-defined relationships between sensory and motor patterns, and each new pattern of motion is regulated by new patterns of activity of the internuncial cells.

It is our opinion that a sensory feedback interpretation of learning and behavior organization such as we have outlined here provides a new context for understanding the educationally significant motions of speech, handwriting, reading, drawing, and other manual skills, as well as the processes and instruments used in training these behavior patterns. Although continuous advances have been made in the last century in developing new methods of auditory and visual communication for educational purposes, there has been no comparable advance in our basic understanding of the function of audiovisual displays in the learning process. The proponents of audiovisual education have never established an adequate theoretical base for research in this area or assessment of existing procedures. The various techniques of auditory and visual communi-

cation—the phonograph, the slide projector, artistically designed books, motion pictures, television—have won wide acceptance but have generated no systematic set of concepts by means of which we can evaluate their significance in education.

Learning theory in education has been —and is—for the most part an extension of standard learning theory in psychology, based on concepts of conditioning and reinforcement. From this point of view, human learning and education are studied and interpreted in terms of methods developed to analyze reinforcement and conditioning in the pigeon, rat, dog, and monkey. We are convinced that these methods and concepts are an inadequate base for understanding how behavior is organized and learned in man, and propose the concepts of neurogeometric theory and the techniques of sensory feedback analysis as an alternative approach.

SUMMARY

1. Delayed sensory feedback produces serious integrative disturbances in all types of motion, as well as emotional disturbances. Many specific effects of delayed auditory and delayed visual feedback are similar.

2. Feedback delay tends to cause continuous motions to degenerate into a series of discrete movements.

3. Although the degree of disturbance is a positive function of the magnitude of delay, there is no one function describing the effect. Rather the shape of the function varies with the task, its organization, the individual, and so forth.

4. Little or no learning occurs under conditions of completely delayed feedback. Moderate learning of tracking performance occurs with the partial delay characteristic of velocity and aided-tracking systems.

5. Future experiments should be carried out to: (a) study blind versus concurrent delay; (b) study visual versus auditory delay; (c) define quantitative functions of delay; (d) analyze perceptual phenomena as effected by delay; (e) study the interaction of spatial and temporal displacement of visual feedback; (f) analyze the regulation of specific motion patterns; and (g) analyze how patterned motion is reorganized by learning.

6. Because the remote control of roving space vehicles will be subject to an unavoidable delay of feedback signals, it is important to institute a program of research to analyze the human factors problems of design and control of such craft.

7. Single factor theories of tracking performance cannot account for its characteristics under different conditions and with different tracking systems. Neurogeometric theory conceptualizes tracking in terms of multidimensional motion patterns controlled by sensory feedback mechanisms, and predicts the deleterious effects of feedback delay.

8. Speech can best be described as a multidimensional motion pattern controlled by different feedback mechanisms. There is evidence that differential detector neurons, such as postulated by neurogeometric theory, exist in the auditory nervous system. We postulate that the on-going patterns of speech are continuously monitored by central detection of spatial and temporal differences in feedback signals.

9. Television experiments on delayed pictorial feedback have been designed in terms of neurogeometric concepts, and to date have supported the theory.

10. Neurogeometric theory and sensory feedback analysis provides a new context for research on human learning and educational procedures.

REFERENCES

1. Andreas, B. G., and Weiss, B.: Review of research on perceptual-motor performance under varied display-control relationships. Dept. of Psychology, Univ. of Rochester, Report No. 2, 1954.
2. Atkinson, C. J.: Adaptation to delayed side-tone. J. Speech Hearing Dis., *18*:386-391, 1953.
3. Bergeijk, W. A. van, and David, E. E., Jr.: Delayed handwriting. Percept. Mot. Skills, *9*:347-357, 1959.
4. Birmingham, H. P., Kahn, A., and Taylor, F. V.: A demonstration of the effects of quickening in multiple-coordinate control tasks. USN Res. Lab. Report No. 4380, 1954.
5. Birmingham, H. P., and Taylor, F. V.: A human engineering approach to the design of man-operated continuous control systems. USN Res. Lab. Report No. 4333, 1954.
6. Black, J. W.: The effect of delayed side-tone upon vocal rate and intensity. J. Speech Hearing Dis., *16*:56-60, 1951.
7. Black, J. W.: The persistence of the effects of delayed side-tone. J. Speech Hearing Dis., *20*:65-68, 1955.
8. Chase, R. A.: Effect of delayed auditory feedback on the repetition of speech sounds. J. Speech Hearing Dis., *23*:583-590, 1958.
9. Chase, R. A., Harvey, S., Standfast, S., Rapin, I., and Sutton, S.: A comparison of the effects of delayed auditory feedback on speech and key-tapping. Communications Lab., Columbia Univ., and Dept. Biometrics Res., State of N. Y., Res. Report, 1958.
10. Chase, R. A., Harvey, S., Standfast, S., Rapin, I., and Sutton, S.: Studies on sensory feedback: The effect of delayed auditory feedback on speech and key-tapping. Communications Lab., Columbia Univ., and Dept. Biometrics Res., State of N. Y., Res. Report, 1959.
11. Chase, R. A., Sutton, S., First, D., and Zubin, J.: A developmental study of changes in behavior under delayed auditory feedback. Communications Lab., Columbia Univ., and Dept. Biometrics Res., State of N. Y., Res. Report, 1959.
12. Chase, R. A., Sutton, S., Rapin, I., Standfast, S., and Harvey, S.: Sensory feedback influences on motor performance. Communications Lab., Columbia Univ., and Dept. Biometrics Res., State of N. Y., Res. Report, 1959.
13. Chernikoff, R., Birmingham, H. P., and Taylor, F. V.: A comparison of pursuit and compensatory tracking under conditions of aiding and no aiding. J. Exp. Psychol., *49*:55-59, 1955.
14. Conklin, J. E.: Effect of control lag on performance in a tracking task. J. Exp. Psychol., *53*:261-268, 1957.
15. Conklin, J. E.: Linearity of the tracking performance function. Percept. Mot. Skills, *9*:387-391, 1959.
16. Davis, H.: Psychophysiology of hearing and deafness. In S. S. Stevens (Editor): Handbook of Experimental Psychology. New York, John Wiley & Sons, Inc., 1951, pp. 1116-1142.
17. Ewert, P. H.: A study of the effect of inverted retinal stimulation upon spatially coordinated behavior. Genet. Psychol. Monogr., 7:177-363, 1930.
18. Fairbanks, G.: Systematic research in experimental phonetics: I. A theory of the speech mechanism as a servosystem. J. Speech Hearing Dis., *19*:133-139, 1954.
19. Fairbanks, G.: Selective vocal effects of delayed auditory feedback. J. Speech Hearing Dis., *20*:333-346, 1955.
20. Fairbanks, G., and Guttman, N.: Effects of

delayed auditory feedback upon articulation. J. Speech Hearing Res., *1*:12-22, 1958.

21. Fitts, P. M.: Engineering psychology and equipment design. In S. S. Stevens (Editor): Handbook of Experimental Psychology. New York, John Wiley & Sons, Inc., 1951, pp. 1287-1340.

22. Foxboro Company. Studies in aided tracking. Nat. Def. Res. Com. Report No. 25, Mem. to Div. 7, 1945.

23. Galambos, R.: Microelectrode studies on the auditory nervous system. Ann. Otol. Rhinol. Laryngol., *66*:503-505, 1957.

24. Galambos, R., and Davis, H.: The response of single auditory-nerve fibers to acoustic stimulation. J. Neurophysiol., *6*:39-58, 1943.

25. Galambos, R., and Davis, H.: Action potentials from single auditory nerve fibers? Science, *108*:513, 1948.

26. Gebhard, J. W.: Some experiments with the VF aided tracking equipment. Appl. Physics Lab., Johns Hopkins Univ., Report No. 166-1-53, 1948.

27. Hanley, C. N., Tiffany, W. R., and Brungard, J. M.: Skin resistance changes accompanying the sidetone test for auditory malingering. J. Speech Hearing Res., *1*: 286-293, 1958.

28. Holland, J. G., and Henson, J. B.: Transfer of training between quickened and unquickened tracking systems. USN Res. Lab. Report No. 4703, 1956.

29. Hull, C. L.: Principles of Behavior: An Introduction to Behavior Theory. New York, Appleton-Century-Crofts, Inc., 1943.

30. Kalmus, H., Denes, P., and Fry, D. B.: Effect of delayed acoustic feed-back on some non-vocal activities. Nature, *175*:1078, 1955.

31. Kalmus, H., Fry, D. B., and Denes, P.: Effects of delayed visual control on writing, drawing, and tracing. Language and Speech, *3*: 96-108, 1960.

32. Kohler, I.: Über Aufbau und Wandlungen der Wahrnehmungswelt, insbesondere über 'bedingte Empfindungen.' Oest. Akad. Wiss., phil.-hist. Klasse Sitzungsber., *227*:(1), 1951. (Translation available by G. Krauthamer.)

33. Kohler, I.: Warum sehen wir aufrecht? Die Pyramide, *2*:30-33, 1951.

34. Kohler, I.: (Rehabituation in perception) Die Pyramide, *5, 6*, and *7*, 1953. (Translation available by H. Gleitman, Ed. by J. J. Gibson.)

35. Kohler, I.: Experiments with prolonged optical distortion. Acta Psychol., *11*:176-178, 1955.

36. Krendel, E. S.: A preliminary study of the power-spectrum approach to the analysis of perceptual-motor performance. USAF Wright Air Dev. Cent. Tech. Report No. 6723, 1951.

37. Lee, B. S.: Some effects of side-tone delay. J. Acoust. Soc. Amer., *22*:639-640, 1950.

38. Lee, B. S.: Effects of delayed speech feedback. J. Acoust. Soc. Amer., *22*:824-826, 1950.

39. Lee, B. S.: Artificial stutter. J. Speech Hearing Dis., *16*:53-55, 1951.

40. Lettvin, J. Y., Maturana, H. R., McCulloch, W. S., and Pitts, W. H.: What the frog's eye tells the frog's brain. Proc. Inst. Rad. Engr., *47*:1940-1951, 1959.

41. Levine, M.: Tracking performance as a function of exponential delay between control and display. USAF Wright Air Dev. Cent. Tech. Report No. 53-236, 1953.

42. Lincoln, R. S.: Instrumental dimensions of motion in relation to training effects in visual pursuit tracking. Unpublished doctoral dissertation, Univ. of Wisconsin, 1952.

43. Lincoln, R. S.: Visual tracking: III. The instrumental dimension of motion in relation to tracking accuracy. J. Appl. Psychol., *37*:489-493, 1953.

44. Lincoln, R. S., and Smith, K. U.: Systematic analysis of factors determining accuracy in visual tracking. Science, *116*:183-187, 1952.

45. Magni, F., Melzack, R., Moruzzi, G., and Smith, C. J.: Direct pyramidal influences on the dorsal-column nuclei. Arch. Ital. Biol., *97*:357-377, 1959.

46. Mechler, E. A., Russell, J. B., and Preston, M. G.: The basis for the optimum aided-tracking time constant. J. Franklin Inst., *248*:327-334, 1949.

47. Pavlov, I. P.: Conditioned reflexes. (Trans. and Ed. by G. V. Anrep.) London, Oxford Univ. Press, 1927.

48. Pearl, B. E., Simon, J. R., and Smith, K. U.: Visual tracking: IV. Interrelations of target speed and aided-tracking ratio in defining tracking accuracy. J. Appl. Psychol., *39*:209-214, 1955.

49. Peters, R. W.: The effect of changes in side-tone delay and level upon rate of oral reading of normal speakers. J. Speech Hearing Dis., *19*:483-490, 1954.

50. Phillips, R. S.: Aided tracking. Radiation Lab., Mass. Inst. Tech., Report No. 453, 1943.

51. Rawnsley. A. I, and Harris, J. D.: Comparative analysis of normal speech and speech with delayed side-tone by means of sound spectrograms. USN Med. Res. Lab. Report No. 248, 1954.

52. Searle, L. V.: Psychological studies of tracking behavior: IV. The intermittency hypothesis as a basis for predicting optimum

aided-tracking time constants. USN Res. Lab. Report No. 3872, 1951.

53. Siipola, E. M.: Studies in mirror drawing. Psychol. Monogr., *46* (No. 6):66-77, 1935.

54. Simon, J. R., and Smith, K. U.: Theory and analysis of component errors in aided pursuit tracking in relation to target speed and aided-tracking time constant. J. Appl. Psychol., *40*:367-370, 1956.

55. Skinner, B. F.: The Behavior of Organisms: An Experimental Analysis. New York, Appleton-Century-Crofts, Inc., 1938.

56. Smith, K. U.: The geometry of human motion and its neural foundations: I. Perceptual and motor adaptation to displaced vision. Amer. J. Phys. Med., *40*:71-87, 1961.

57. Smith, K. U.: The geometry of human motion and its neural foundations: II. Neurogeometric theory and its experimental basis. Amer. J. Phys. Med., *40*:109-129, 1961.

58. Smith, K. U., and Bloom, R.: The electronic handwriting analyzer and motion study of writing. J. Appl. Psychol., *40*:302-306, 1956.

59. Smith, K. U., and Bridgman, M.: The neural mechanisms of movement vision and optic nystagmus. J. Exp. Psychol., *33*:165-187, 1943.

60. Smith, K. U., Kappauf, W. E., and Bojar, S.: The functions of the visual cortex in optic nystagmus at different velocities of movement in the visual field. J. Gen. Psychol., *22*:341-357, 1940.

61. Smith, K. U., and Smith, W. M.: The Behavior of Man: Introduction to Psychology. New York, Henry Holt & Company, Inc., 1958.

62. Smith, K. U., and Smith, W. M.: Perception and Motion: An Analysis of Space-Structured Behavior. Philadelphia, W. B. Saunders Company, 1962.

63. Smith, K. U., and Warkentin, J.: The central neural organization of optic functions related to minimum visible acuity. J. Genet. Psychol., *55*:177-195, 1939.

64. Smith, K. U., and Wehrkamp, R.: A universal motion analyzer applied to psycho-

motor performance. Science *113*:242-244, 1951.

65. Smith, W. M., McCrary, J. W., and Smith, K. U.: Delayed visual feedback and behavior. Science, *132*:1013-1014, 1960.

66. Smith, W. M., Smith, K. U., Stanley, R., and Harley, W.: Analysis of performance in televised visual fields: Preliminary report. Percept. Mot. Skills, *6*:195-198, 1956.

67. Snyder, F. W., and Pronko, N. H.: Vision with spatial inversion. Wichita, Univ. of Wichita Press, 1952.

68. Sobczyk, A.: Aided tracking. Radiation Lab., Mass. Inst. Tech., Report No. 430 and Suppl. Report No. 452, 1943.

69. Spilka, B.: Some vocal effects of different reading passages and time delays in speech feedback. J. Speech Hearing Dis., *19*:37-47, 1954.

70. Stetson, R. H.: Motor Phonetics: A Study of Speech Movements in Action. Amsterdam, N. Holland Publ. Co., 1951.

71. Stratton, G. M.: Some preliminary experiments in vision without inversion of the retinal image. Psychol. Rev., *3*:611-617, 1896.

72. Stratton, G. M.: Vision without inversion of the retinal image. Psychol. Rev., *4*:341-360; 463-481, 1897.

73. Stratton, G. M.: The spatial harmony of touch and sight. Mind, *8*:463-505, 1899.

74. Thorndike, E. L.: Animal Intelligence. New York, The Macmillan Company, 1911.

75. Thorndike, E. L.: Educational Psychology. II. The Psychology of Learning. New York, Teachers College, Columbia Univ., 1913.

76. Tiffany, W. R., and Hanley, C. N.: Adaptation to delayed side-tone. J. Speech Hearing Dis., *21*:164-172, 1956.

77. Warrick, M. J.: Effect of transmission-type control lags on tracking accuracy. USAF Air Mat. Com. Tech. Report No. 5916, 1949.

78. Winchester, R. A., Gibbons, E. W., and Krebs, D. F.: Adaptation to sustained delayed side-tone. J. Speech Hearing Dis., *24*: 25-28, 1951.

INDEX